STO

RANGATIRA

THE AUTHORS

Norman B. Tindale has been Curator of Anthropology at the South Australian Museum since 1926. As a Carnegie Fellow, he has travelled and studied in Europe and the United States. During World War II he served in the Royal Australian Air Force and in the United States Military Intelligence, where his knowledge of Japanese proved invaluable. In 1956 the Royal Society of South Australia gave him its Verco Medal for his contributions to science.

Harold A. Lindsay collaborated with Norman Tindale in writing a children's book concerning the Negritos, who were the earliest inhabitants of Australia and lived at the end of the Ice Age. This story, *The First Walkabout*, won Australia's 1956 award as the best juvenile of the year. He has spent much of his time exploring remote Australian regions, studying anthropology, and writing for periodicals and radio. He is a member of the Anthropological Society of South Australia.

A Polynesian Saga

RANGATIRA
(The High-born)

by

NORMAN B. TINDALE

and

HAROLD A. LINDSAY

illustrated by

DOUGLAS F. MAXTED

FRANKLIN WATTS, INC.
A Division of THE GROLIER SOCIETY INC.
575 LEXINGTON AVENUE, NEW YORK 22, N.Y.

Composed in Caledonia type and printed by
Western Printing Services Ltd, Bristol
Made in Great Britain

CONTENTS

Publisher's Note

Because they think you will enjoy this book more if you know how to pronounce the names the authors have provided a Pronunciation Guide, which will be found at page 184.

1

THE COMING OF REHUA

Kura was the only person on the island to sight the canoe as it came through the gap in the reef. A heavy squall of rain was drifting to leeward, leaving the hibiscus bushes and banana plants gleaming wetly, while big drops pattered down from the drooping leaf-plumes of the coconut palms. Through the thinning veil of rain she saw the blurred outline of the triangular brown sail.

She had been gathering pandanus leaves for the mat which she was weaving, and had sheltered from the shower under an overhanging rock above the beach. Her dark brown eyes, wide with fear, stared at the approaching craft. None of the fishing-canoes was out that morning, so it must be a stranger. Were men from the neighbouring island of Oamu, the hereditary foes of her people, making a surprise attack?

She ran along the beach until the village came into view, then screamed, "Te pahi! Te pahi!"

Only one man heard that cry of "Canoe!" The thick-necked, hulking Pararaka had been squatting in the canoe-house, a big koa-wood club in his hands and a heavy scowl on his lowering features. He longed to be a warrior chief, leading parties of fighting-men on raids—but what opportunities did he have on this island?

The distant cry brought him to his feet. He gave a glance to seaward, roused the village with a shout, then went bounding down the beach. Here was a chance to distinguish himself at last!

Kura's fear died as the rain ceased and the canoe came

into plain view. It wasn't a big one, leading a fleet of war-craft filled with fighting-men. It was small and carried only one man. Pararaka arrived, panting from his run, to stand with his lower lip thrust out and his club ready.

When the canoe was close inshore Kura saw that the man in it was old, with grey hair. The unfamiliar designs tattooed on his skin showed that he belonged to some far-off island, while the gaunt face and emaciated body indicated that he had been long at sea.

Pararaka was disappointed. Here was his first chance to kill a man—but what credit was there in slaying an old one? Still, it would be practice.... He waited until the tiny craft grounded in the shallows, then stepped forward with his teeth bared. Behind him there was a cry of protest and Kura splashed past, to turn and bar the way.

"Don't you dare hurt him!" she said fiercely, her hands clenched and her chest heaving.

"Out of the way!" Pararaka snarled, trying to dodge around her. A glance towards the beach had shown him that the men from the village would be here in a few moments—and one of the lesser chiefs might claim the right to kill this stranger.

Kura, her eyes flashing angrily, managed to keep between the bloodthirsty young warrior and his intended victim. Pararaka snarled threats, but Kura refused to give way.

"I'm a high-born Rangatira!" she reminded him. "You know what will happen if a low-born person like you harms me!"

He made a last attempt to get past her, then the first men arrived and a voice with a ring of authority ordered him to come ashore. Pararaka obeyed sullenly. The gathering crowd waited, staring at the stranger. Old Hikurangi, high chief of the island, was coming slowly along the beach, and the final word would lie with him. Pararaka went to meet Hikurangi.

"I claim the right to kill him. I was here first!" he said.

"Kill him?" repeated the old chief, leaning on his carved walking-staff. "Why?"

"What use is he?" Pararaka said scornfully.

"An old but wise man is of more use than a young one with big muscles and small sense!" Hikurangi retorted.

"Stand aside!" He moved close to the canoe, noting how the castaway scorned to plead for mercy. "This one may be an ariki, first-born of noble parents, such as I am myself," he said to the lesser chiefs. "Carry him to my house. My women will care for him."

Several men hurried to obey. Pararaka walked away with a sulky air, his club whistling as he made practice swings with it. Hikurangi listened to the men who had been the first to arrive, heard what Kura had done, and then gave the girl a glance of approval which brought a flush to her light brown cheeks.

He paced slowly back to the village behind the group which carried the wasted figure, while the young men hauled the canoe ashore and discussed its build and rig.

Within a few days Rehua, the stranger, had recovered sufficiently to take a seat in the council house. There he related to the assembled chiefs a story which was all too common in the Pacific 800 years ago. A fleet of war-canoes from Oropana had attacked his island of Matatuki. Taken by surprise, for the raiders had landed at night, his people had been killed or driven into the hills. "All my brave sons were slain," cried the old man, tears rolling down his wrinkled cheeks. "They died trying to save their mother, wives, and sisters. Even my little grandchildren were killed. Of my household, only I escaped.

"After dark on the following night I crept close to the camp of our attackers. I heard them planning to hunt down the survivors in the morning, sparing only the prettiest of the girls, whom they would take home with them.

"I saw it would be useless to rally our surviving warriors. How could a few tens overcome hundreds? I went to the little fishing-canoe which had belonged to one of my sons, put into it all the coconuts I could find in the dark, and sailed away."

The assembled chiefs nodded. The savagery of the men of Oropana was known to them by hearsay.

"I had intended to go to the near-by island of Otupu, whose high chief was my friend, to ask him to bring his warriors to attack the men of Oropana before they could get away, but the wind was adverse. My strength gave out when I tried to paddle against it. I had to let the canoe drift.

"When the coconuts I had with me were used I found others floating on the sea. I caught rainwater with my sail. Finally I sighted your island and steered for it, hoping you would let me live with you."

"This island is yours," Hikurangi assured him, then congratulated him on making such a long voyage in a tiny canoe.

"It would have been impossible for an ordinary man,"

Rehua said proudly, "but I am a great canoe chief! Three times, steering by the stars Karewa, Puanga, and Whanui, have I navigated an ocean-going canoe to a far-off island and sailed back again to my people. I have even voyaged, as Kupe did, to the great land of Aotearoa. You have heard of Kupe?"

Those present knew of the Polynesian Columbus, but only as a legendary figure who had lived many generations before they were born. This island, they explained, lay far off the regular sailing routes. Few visitors ever came there to bring news.

"Kupe made many long voyages," their guest informed them. "One took him to the island of Rarotonga. There he saw many small, long-tailed birds with shining feathers arrive from the south-west. They were weary from a long flight across the ocean, so Kupe knew they had come from a far-off land."

A glance at the men in the council house showed Rehua that they were listening with breathless interest.

"The people of Rarotonga told Kupe that the birds always arrived at the same time each year, to fly home again before the season of the big rains began. Kupe resolved to seek the land from which they came.

"He overhauled his canoe *Matahorua*, placed food and water aboard, then set sail, accompanied by his wife, Hine-te-Aparinga, his friend Ngahue, and a crew of picked men."

Rehua went on to relate a story which his people had passed on from generation to generation for hundreds of years, and which was destined to be preserved until the day, seven centuries later, when European men heard it and wrote it down.

Day after day the big canoe, its matting sail filled by the steady trade wind, sailed down the Ara-Moana path-of-the-sea on a south-west course, but there was never a sight of land. The crew began to fear that only empty wastes of ocean lay ahead, in which they would perish when their supplies of food and water were exhausted.

But Kupe refused to put about. Land must lie ahead! Had not the direction taken by other flocks of migrating birds led canoe chiefs to find and colonize islands all over the great Ocean-of-Kiwa? "Stop this grumbling!" he said sternly. "Watch for signs of land. It must be near now."

A few mornings later Hine-te-Aparinga, taking her turn as look-out, raised a joyful cry of "He Ao!" The crew sprang from their sleeping-places to gaze in the direction indicated by her pointing arm.

On the rim of the horizon and just visible in the first pale dawn light was a cloud which hung in one spot while all the others drifted steadily across the sky—a land cloud at last! In the afternoon they sighted the hills of the island which they named Aotearoa: Land-of-Long-Bright-Days.

They sailed around the new land, anchoring in sheltered bays and going ashore to examine a country where everything was new and strange. No people lived there, but they saw great moa birds, some taller than a man. Ngahue killed one and preserved some of the meat in a gourd of melted fat, so that he could take it home and show it to his people. He also took a piece of the skin, covered with fine, hairlike feathers.

After Kupe had sailed around the three islands of the vast new land he returned to Tahiti-Nui and told his people of the wonders which had been seen. If anyone else wanted to reach Aotearoa, he said, you sailed in the moon before the coming of the wet season and laid a course which kept the setting sun and the evening star a little to the right of the bow of the canoe.

Rehua paused at this point in his story, for he was still very weak, and talking tired him. The assembled chiefs looked at one another, the same thought in every mind. After a short rest Rehua went on to say:

"In my big canoe *Awa-Potaka* I followed the sailing directions which my people have handed down from Kupe's day. Aotearoa is no longer uninhabited, I found. Some of those who live there now are descended from people who followed Kupe's course. Great storms had driven the canoes of others to the new land.

"Those people are few, though. One can walk for days over wide lands which none claim. In a river on the west coast of the south island of the new land we found the wonderful stone described by Kupe. It has been named 'pounamu,' for it is the colour of the sea where the water is shallow. It makes far better blades for adzes and chisels than any other stone. We took pieces of it home with us." He shook his head sadly.

"It was a dangerous possession. We showed our new tools to visitors from other islands. The men of Oropana heard about them and attacked us to get those tools of pounamu stone."

Again the assembled chiefs looked at one another. For the past two generations the island had been faced with a very serious problem. The population kept increasing, but the food-supply was limited. Much of the land was crag, cliff, or steep, rocky slope. Only in three gullies were there swampy spots suitable for the growing of taro, while few patches of hillside were fertile enough for the kumara sweet potato.

The big red-gold fei plantains grew sparsely on the slopes of the central mountain. At the back of the island's one beach was their only grove of coconuts, with, behind it, on a strip of level land, their one plantation of breadfruit-trees. During most of the wet season sudden storms made it too rough for their canoes to fish in the waters outside the sheltering reef.

For years they had been discussing the possibility of easing the pressure of population by sending thirty of their young men and women on a voyage to seek a new home—

but always there had been the problem of knowing where a new land could be found. Now the gods had sent them a great navigator to pilot the canoe carrying the migrants!

How fortunate that Kura had prevented the stupid, bloodthirsty Pararaka from killing Rehua!

They began to confer, but soon saw that their guest was exhausted. "We'll talk of this again to-morrow evening," said Hikurangi, motioning two of the younger men to assist Rehua to his sleeping-mats.

Three boys, who had been squatting outside the council house and listening to the talk of the chiefs, commented on what they had overheard.

"It must be wonderful to sail far across the ocean and find new lands, as Kupe did," said Maui, gazing up at the stars which Rehua had mentioned as aids to navigation.

"Don't suppose we'd stand a chance of going if they send some people away in a great canoe," Hauka remarked, patting the head of the kuri dog which had come frisking up to lick at his face.

"You won't catch me going," said Tatau, yawning and stretching. "Didn't you hear old Rehua say you had only one drink a day on a long voyage? And what about the canoes he mentioned which sailed off and were never heard of again! I'm staying right here!"

For over an hour that night Maui lay on his sleeping-mats, listening to the grunting and squealing of the pigs as they rooted for food on the hillside above the village and the dull, booming rumble of the surf as it broke on the reef which sheltered the bay. His thoughts roved to the legends which Uropaki, the Tohunga priest, taught in the Whare-Wananga House of Learning.

Always, it seemed, his people had been a race of voyagers, sailing off in search of new lands to colonize as each island became overcrowded. How he would love to go on one of those trips! He liked sailing. He often went out in one of the fishing-canoes, learning how to manage the little craft and to locate the schools of big fish by watching for the sea-birds which hung over them.

Deep-sea fishing was a tough way to obtain food, especially if you had to paddle home against a head-wind. It was hot out on the open sea in the middle of the day, too, even if you plastered your hair with burnt coral lime to shield your head from the heat of the sun. Still, it was real man's work. . . . But how much more exciting it must be to sail a big canoe towards the end of the world!

Did the world have an end? Uropaki said it just went on for ever. But, if that were true, where were the ends of the tunnel under the earth through which the sun passed during the hours of darkness, to appear again in the east each morning?

There were many of these puzzling things. When your own time came and Hine-Nui-te-Po, the Great Lady of the Night, led you to the spirit world, from which nobody returned, did you meet all those who had died before you?

Why couldn't you see far across the ocean when you stood on the beach, yet when you climbed to the top of the mountain you could see a long way—even as far as the hills on the island of Oamu, which was out of sight at sea-level . . .

Perhaps old Rehua knew the answers to some of these things. He must get his father to ask him. . . .

Maui fell asleep, to dream that he had grown to manhood and was in command of a great canoe which had sailed to a wonderful new land. There he met Tane-Mahuta, God of the Forests, who gave answers to all the things which were puzzling him.

But when Maui awakened next morning he strove in vain to remember the god's explanations.

2

THE DECISION OF REHUA

When the first light of dawn appeared the little roosters perched in the trees at the rear of the village raised the screeching cry which they had inherited from their jungle-fowl ancestors. Their noise awakened Kura. She yawned, then surrendered to the temptation of spending a few more luxurious moments on her sleeping-mats.

"Don't forget the tide. It'll be flowing soon," warned her mother.

Kura stood up, put on her skirt of ribbon-like hibiscus bark and collected her fishing-gear: a large, pot-shaped cane basket with a hinged lid and a long, pliant 'come here' stick. To protect her feet from the sharp coral she bound them with strips of plaited coconut fibre.

From her corner of the family food basket she took the remains of the previous night's supper; a piece of baked taro, half a cooked plantain and the claw of a coconut-crab. Walking to the adjoining house, she called to her friends Hina and Ngaio. While waiting for them to appear she placed the crab claw on the edge of the house platform and cracked the shell with a stone.

Hina was very drowsy. She kept blinking and yawning until they had washed their faces in the freshwater creek pool at the far end of the village. At the palm grove they waited impatiently for the boys to appear. When they came in sight, strolling along with a casual air and carrying baskets and digging-sticks, Kura called to them.

"Hurry up, or we'll miss the tide!"

Hauka and Tatau took no notice, but Maui broke into

a run. When he arrived at the palms he took a cord from around his waist, looped it over the instep of each of his feet, and put his arms around a trunk.

After drawing up his feet he pressed their soles against opposite sides of the palm and straightened his body. The cord which linked his feet prevented them from slipping. Again he drew up his feet, and so he mounted the trunk with an action like that of a frog swimming. Soon he was under the leafy crown high above, sawing through the stems of green coconuts with the edge of a mussel shell.

One after another, six huge nuts came down, thudding into the litter of old fronds placed at the foot of the tree to break their fall. As Maui slid down the tree each girl put a drinking-nut into her basket and hurried off along the beach. The boys took the remaining nuts and went up the track which led to a sweet-potato garden on the hill above.

At the far end of the beach the reef, bared by the tide, was close to the shore. Here there was a raft made from the cork-light trunks of white hibiscus trees. The girls launched it, poled it across the open water, lifted it on to the reef and set off along the broad rampart of coral. When they reached the spot where the surf rolled in heavily they put the drinking-nuts in the shade of a coral boulder to keep them cool.

"I've got something to tell you!" Hina said suddenly. "I've just remembered. I woke up when Father came home from the council last night. I heard him tell Mother they would be building a great big canoe, then some of the people will sail off in it to find a new home somewhere far away! It made me so excited. I couldn't get to sleep again for a long time."

Kura and Ngaio were startled by the news. Would any of the young people take part in the great adventure? They discussed this exciting prospect until the rising sun reminded them that they had work to do. Already they could

B

see other girls at work along the far end of the southern reef.

Kura picked her way across the coral to a deep hole and peered into the green water. She located a likely-looking crevice and lowered her 'come here' stick to probe it. As the pliant wand entered the cranny she twisted and shook it.

Presently came the feeling that the stick had become entangled in something yielding yet clinging. She continued to shake and twist it. Then a long tentacle came out, gripping the stick as it sought for the live thing which was causing the movements. Another arm followed, then more of them, and finally the bag-like body of the octopus appeared.

With her free hand Kura made sure that the lid of her tall basket was open. The octopus crept farther up the vibrating stick. Finally she whipped it out of the water and held the creature over the mouth of the basket. The octopus released its grip and dropped inside, where it writhed, changed colour, and exuded a slimy black fluid. Kura closed the lid and latched it.

"You're always lucky," Hina complained. "A lovely big one just got away from me."

"I'm only finding baby ones," said Ngaio.

As the sun climbed up the sky the heat increased rapidly. Presently the girls went to their drinking-nuts and with the edge of a clam shell hacked the top off one. It revealed a white-lined, globular interior filled to the brim with clear, sweetish water. They drank from it in turn, and then Hina tossed the empty nut into the breakers.

By the time they had emptied the last nut the tide had begun to flow. The final task was to haul up the family fish-traps. They were drum-shaped affairs woven from cane, with an inward-pointing funnel at each end. Hina wailed when hers held only a huge, useless porcupine-fish and a lot of small crabs, but Ngaio squealed with delight, for hers held a huge, speckled coral cod.

Kura was nearly as fortunate. Her catch was a banded lobster and four medium-sized bream. They filled her basket, for it already held five octopuses. After smashing up the crabs they put the meat from them into the bait baskets which hung in the centre of each trap, then let them sink again into deep water.

"I'll hear complaints when I get home," said Hina, as they hurried back to the shore ahead of the rising tide. Her basket held a solitary octopus. After the raft had been carried up the beach Kura opened her creel and took out a bream and an octopus.

"There," she said, as she dropped them into Hina's basket. Ngaio also contributed an octopus. Hina hugged her friends by way of thanks. After taking home their catches they washed the perspiration and sea-salt from their bodies at the freshwater bathing-pool.

All the other fishing girls went off to lie down, but Kura decided to work on the fine mat which she was weaving. She felt tired, but with a little luck the weaving would be finished by the middle of the afternoon—and she did want to hear the favourable comments of the old women when her mother took it around for inspection.

A few hours previously, when the three boys had

climbed the stile over the fence which kept the pigs from entering the sweet-potato patch, Maui had gone to work at the far end of the plot. He wanted to think, and you couldn't do it with a couple of friends chattering beside you. To-morrow morning there would be a session in the House of Learning—and as likely as not Uropaki would call on somebody to recite a lesson. He would probably be the one selected.

Uropaki was bound to choose religion as the subject, Maui thought, as he grubbed up weeds and loosened the topsoil with his digging-stick. They hadn't dealt with the gods for some weeks. He decided to rehearse what he would have to say.

Above all the unseen beings who ruled the world stood Io, the parentless, whose name was so holy that it must be mentioned only in a reverent whisper. From him descended all other gods, including Rangi the Sky Father and Papa the Earth Mother. For long ages these two had clung together, shutting off all light from their children. Finally Tane, one of their sons, had grown restless.

He wanted to let in the light so he could see the world clearly. He parted his parents by thrusting Rangi far into the sky, where he has lived ever since. Then light descended on the great Earth Mother.

But the separated lovers have never ceased to mourn for each other. When rain falls the drops are Rangi's tears, while the white mists which rise f om the breast of Papa at dawn are her arms, reaching upward in a vain search for the lost lover who now dwells among the stars.

Before long Tane felt very lonely. He could now see the world around him, but he had no companion to share it.

Finally he took some earth, moulded it into the figure of a beautiful being, breathed upon it, and it came to life as the first woman; Hine-Ahu-One, the Earth-formed Maid. Tane married her, and their son Tiki was the first mortal man. His sister, Hine-Nui-te-Po, descended to the spirit world, and there takes into her loving care the souls of the dead.

When he came to the end of the recital Maui felt confident of being able to repeat it without a mistake.

It grew steamy in the clearing after the sun had risen above the surrounding trees. Sweat beaded the skins of the three boys as they worked among the vegetable plants. At last they finished their task, emptied the remaining drinking-nut, and set off for home, carrying baskets of ripe yellow tubers dug from under the older plants.

When they reached the village they put the baskets in the shade and ran down the beach for a swim. They were very hungry when they came out of the water. Each ate a bowl of the custard-like poi breadfruit paste, then they and every one else in the village, except Kura at her mat-weaving and a few old men who kept watch in case a fleet of enemy war-canoes appeared, unrolled their sleeping-mats and dozed through the midday heat.

When the sun was half-way down the western sky the boys stirred. Some brought firewood, while others cleaned out the stone-lined cooking-pits and lit fires in them. When they had burned down, the ashes were shovelled out with sheets of bark, then a thick layer of green leaves was laid in the bottom of each pit and sprinkled with water.

On this steaming bed they laid the vegetables; turnip-like taro, plantains resembling huge red bananas, rough-skinned breadfruit, and oddly shaped sweet potatoes. Above there were placed long-legged coconut crabs, octopus tentacles, and cleaned fish, each wrapped in banana leaf.

More leaves were laid over the food, with another sprinkling of water, a large mat went on top, and the earth was heaped over it to shut in the heat. Then the boys ran off to pick sides for a sham fight on the beach, leaving the food to steam-bake.

The boys returned when the shadows were long. They opened the umo oven pits and selected the choicest pieces, which the girls served on platters of palm leaf to the chiefs. When all the leading men had finished their suppers they strolled off to the council house, there to carry out the ceremonial drinking of kava as a preliminary to discussing village affairs.

Then the rest of the men were served, followed by the women and girls. Finally, as the swift tropic dusk came down, the hungry boys ate what was left, reserving a snack for their breakfasts.

Maui, Hauka, Tatau, and a few other boys then crept down to the council house, where they squatted just outside the palm-leaf blinds and listened to what was being said. They heard the high chief inquire, "Will you design a great ocean-going canoe for us, see that she is built properly, and then navigate her to this land of Aotearoa, taking some of our younger people to find a new home there?"

Rehua considered the matter, his chin sunk on his chest and his eyes closed. Such a voyage involved great hardships—and he was now an old man, entitled to peace and rest for whatever span of life was left to him. Sad to think that all his fine sons were dead and his people killed, except some girls carried off to slavery. . . .

Still, this offered him one last great adventure. Perhaps it would make these people cherish his memory. He raised his head and looked at Hikurangi.

"I shall do it," he said quietly.

A murmur of admiration and gratitude came from the circle of men.

"But to build such a canoe is a great undertaking," Rehua warned them. "First comes preparing to grow more food. The men who build the canoe will have no time to go out fishing or to work in the gardens. Nor will the women and girls have time for mat-weaving, gossiping, flower-gathering, or dancing. The boys will have something more important to do than sham fights or swimming."

He ran his gaze over the faces of the chiefs, illuminated by the bluish, flickering glow of a candlenut torch.

"Even the old ones must do their share. Great coils of sinnet cord must be prepared for lashings. Paddles must be made. It will take months to carve the figurehead and stern-piece. A great anchor stone must be chipped into shape and a big, strong rope made to go with it."

They listened with grave attention; then arose the question of who would be chosen to make the voyage. Before anyone could speak Hikurangi motioned for silence and pointed significantly to the outside of the house. A lesser chief rose from his stack of mats with a casual air, then made a sudden spring through the doorway. He found nearly a dozen boys outside.

"Go away!" he said sternly. "Some things are not for your ears!"

When nobody remained within hearing one chief stated that this would be a grand opportunity to get rid of all the lazy, quarrelsome, and incompetent members of the little community. "They will find better opportunities in a new land—and we'll be happier without them," he explained.

It seemed a good idea to several others, but Rehua wouldn't hear of it. You didn't send away your worthless people. Only your very best ones could man a canoe bound on so long a voyage, or hope to succeed when the destination was reached.

"Think of all the work awaiting them when they arrive at Aotearoa," he said earnestly. "Houses to be built, gardens dug and fenced, fishing-canoes made, game to be hunted. How can lazy people and poor workmen do it all?"

He paused to hear comments, but there were none.

"Those you send must be good warriors, too," he went on. "There will be only fifteen men in the crew, so each must be able to fight well if a battle is forced upon them."

The council bowed to his judgment, but their hearts

were sad. They would have to part wth their most promising sons and their fairest daughters!

"Such things cannot be helped," said Hikurangi, "so it is no use grieving. As Rehua says, the people who go to this new land must be brave, skilful, and resourceful. The women who accompany them must be talented and hard-working. But it will be a great honour to be chosen." He sighed, then added regretfully, "If I could be young again I would be the first to volunteer."

He went on to deal with the matter of the production of extra food. Every plot of good soil, even one no larger than the house in which they sat, must be cleared and planted. It would have to start at once.

At dawn next morning Maui was awakened by an unusual stir and bustle. Men were renewing the lashings on their stone-bladed adzes and sharpening digging-sticks, while the younger women were preparing to take over the weeding and cultivating of the plots now planted.

"You won't be going to the House of Learning to-day," said Maui's father. "There'll be no lessons for a long time. Rehua needs a guide to show him where our best trees grow—and somebody to take messages. I told him you were a smart boy—and you'd better live up to it! Get ready —he'll be here soon."

3

THE GREAT TREE

Rehua was still very weak and shaky. Leaning heavily on a staff, he would walk a short distance, then pause to regain his breath. "I can't help it, boy," the old man panted, after they had ascended a rise in the path. "I was a long time in that canoe. Sometimes I went two or three days with nothing to eat or drink."

Maui studied the old man's face. The designs tattooed on it gave him a fierce expression, yet under it there was something kindly. "Would you mind if I asked questions, Chief?" he said.

"What do you wish to know, Maui?"

"The men all say you are very wise in the ways of the sea. I'd like to learn all I can about canoe-building and why things are done."

Rehua gave him a smile of approval. "If the old ones don't pass on their knowledge, how can the young ones learn?" he agreed. He scanned the surrounding timber. "Find me a young tamanu-tree. At the height of your head from the ground it must be about as big as your waist. It must grow close to a much larger tree."

Maui ran off, but the search took a long time. Finally he found what was required. He helped Rehua to climb the hillside to where it grew.

"Good!" said the old man. "Mark it by chopping off bark with your adze. This is to be an outrigger boom for the great canoe. Why must a bigger tree grow close to it?"

Maui tried to puzzle it out, but failed to think of the right answer.

"The outrigger booms of fishing-canoes. Are they straight?" Rehua inquired.

"No. They're curved, like this." Maui bent a stick to show what he meant, then looked at the selected tree. It was straight now and would have to be bent to shape. But the combined strength of all the men on the island couldn't bend one that size.... Then he realized how it would be done.

"I know, Chief! We'll put a thick rope around the top of this tree and the trunk of that big one. Then we'll put a strong stick through the loop and twist the rope. That'll pull the little tree over and put a bend in it." He frowned as another thought came to him. Being green, the smaller trunk would straighten again when the rope was removed.

"You're right," Rehua said encouragingly. "It's done a little at a time, of course. Every few days we twitch the rope a bit tighter."

"But the bend won't stay in green wood, Chief——"

"We'll make it stay. When the tree reaches the right curve a man will ringbark it. That makes it die, and when it has dried out the curve stops in it." He glanced at the forest ahead.

"There must be two booms. Find another pair of trees." Maui located them, and then searched for those from which the topside planking of the canoe would be hewn. As each was located it was marked with the adze.

"Now show me the great tree of which your high chief spoke," said the old man.

Maui led him to the head of the valley, where the rock walls closed in to form a gorge. Here, close to the spring which fed the head-waters of the little creek, grew a mighty tamanu-tree, far larger than any other on the island. Rehua gazed at the great, lichen-splotched trunk. It was nearly the height of a man in thickness!

He glanced up to the spreading limbs, festooned with long beards of moss and with orchids and ferns growing wherever a fork provided a pocket of decaying leaves. Ten man-heights to the first branch! It was indeed a wonderful tree! But was the trunk solid?

"Fetch me a stone from the creek-bed. One as large as a husked coconut," he ordered. When Maui brought it he found that Rehua had used the adze to chip off the bark in four places around the butt of the tree.

His head on one side and holding his breath in order to hear clearly, Rehua struck each patch of bared wood with the stone. In every case there was the sharp, clear crack of solid timber beneath the blow.

"It is a wonderful tree!" Rehua said happily. "From it we shall make one of the biggest and best canoes ever to sail down the Ara-Moana sea-path!" He glanced upward as a shadow came over the sun, to see heavy clouds massing about the craggy peak of the island's central mountain.

"We must hurry back. It will be raining soon," he said. As they passed down the valley they heard men's voices and the thudding of adzes as tree roots were hacked through. The land for the new garden plots was being cleared.

"Your people will be very weary by the time this canoe is built and launched," Rehua remarked. "It is a great undertaking."

"You'll let me go on being your helper, Chief?"

"You think you'll find it more interesting than building fences around new gardens and pulling up weeds?"

"Yes—and I want to be a canoe chief like you when I grow up, too."

Rehua's eyes misted, and he averted his head. Once his sons had been like this bright-faced, eager lad. It was still hard to realize that they had all been killed. He walked on without speaking for a time.

"You'll be my helper," he promised at length.

At the village they went to the workshop house, where Apiroa, the chief of the craftsmen, had laid out some slabs of basalt rock for inspection, with, beside them, some baskets of round, fist-sized stones. All had proved their toughness by surviving the pounding of the surf at the foot of the cliffs on the windward side of the island.

Maui watched while each slab was hung in a noose of cord and struck with one of the smaller stones, with Rehua and Apiroa listening to the ringing note which it gave out.

"Which is the best?" Rehua inquired suddenly.

"Both those sounded good to me," Maui replied, pointing to a couple.

"You will be a craftsman some day," Apiroa agreed. He stood one of the selected slabs on end, bade an assistant hold it steady, took a round rock from a basket and struck a blow with it. The only result was a small, whitish spot at the point of impact. He struck again and again; finally the hammer-stone shattered in his hand.

"The blade made from that piece of rock won't break when used," Rehua commented.

Apiroa selected another hammer-stone and tried again. This time he knocked off a long flake. A further battering detached more flakes, and gradually the shapeless rock was trimmed into a huge chisel blade, as long as a man's arm from elbow to fingertips and as wide as the palm of a hand.

For some time big raindrops had been pattering on the thatch overhead; now a heavy shower roared on the roof and sent curtains of water cascading from the eaves. The men came running from their tasks of clearing land and set about preparing tools for canoe-building.

Flat slabs of stone were laid on the floor of the workshop, each accompanied by a close-woven basket of coarse sand and gourds of water. Some of the men sprinkled sand on the grinding-stones, wetted it, and began to rub adze and chisel blades to and fro on the grit to sharpen them. Others chipped and scraped at a long, straight piece of the hard, strong reddish-brown koa wood.

It was twice a man-height in length and would be the thickness of an arm below the elbow when finished, except at one end, where it swelled to the size of a leg above the knee.

"That will be the shaft of the great chisel with which we'll fell the trees," Rehua told Maui.

Day after day the same programme was followed. At dawn the men hurried out to clear, fence, and plant the new gardens. When the rain set in towards noon they came to work in the hut. As he ran errands for Rehua or stood by for orders Maui saw bustle and activity everywhere.

On the beach slabs of husk from ripe coconuts were buried in wet sand to rot the pith from the fibres. In the houses some of the old men rubbed the prepared fibres on their bare thighs to spin string, while others plaited these lengths of twine into sinnet cord. More old men wove additional fish-traps from cane.

The girls had no time for mat-making, weaving flower garlands, romping, or practising dance steps. They had a brief rest after their daily fishing; then they climbed around on the mountain slopes, gathering the long, narrow pandanus leaves from which the sail of the big canoe would be woven. When sufficient leaves had been collected they peeled the bark from aute saplings, stripped off the inner layer, made it into bundles, and put them to soak in the creek in order to remove the slimy sap.

After they had been cleaned the girls took these strips and built them into a thick, overlapping layer upon a smooth, round log. This was beaten with little four-sided mallets made from a very heavy black wood. Gradually the sheet would felt and thin out, until it became tapa cloth, strong and soft.

The little mallets clinked musically while this work was in progress, but Maui always hurried past the hut where the cloth was being made, his head averted. It was tapu for a man to look upon any of the unfinished material. Only after it had been dried, bleached, and the pretty designs had been stencilled on it could a man handle and wear tapa.

When the big stone chisel-blade had been chipped into shape the long haft was polished by being rubbed down with dried sharkskin, then the blade was lashed to a shoulder on the thick end with layer upon layer of cord. The final step was grinding the cutting edge.

Four strong men gripped the haft and rubbed the blade to and fro on a broad slab of stone, while Maui scattered sand to serve as the abrasive and Hauka sprinkled it with water. Gradually the hard, sharp grains of sand ground the blade to an edge. When Rehua had given the huge tool a final inspection Uropaki, the priest, heaved it on to his shoulder and staggered off up the track which led to the great tamanu-tree.

In the gorge he laid his heavy burden in a little cave, there to sleep for the night. Standing before it, he chanted a prayer in which he beseeched the mana of the god Tane to enter it during the night and give it strength for its work.

Next morning the tree-felling began. The last rains of the wet season had fallen a few days previously, and now a steady sailing-wind blew from the south-east, driving all the steamy heat from the forest, rattling the long leaves of the coconut palms, and making every one feel energetic. Gone were the heavy rainclouds which had piled up nearly every afternoon for months. In their place small, soft white ones drifted high in the sky.

All the undergrowth had been cleared from the base of the great tree and the ground built into a level platform with stones and earth. The six strongest men on the island stood in two rows facing each other, with the long haft of the felling chisel between them. Keeping time by means of a song, they swung the tool a few times, then drove the edge like a battering-ram into the trunk.

Again they struck, this time at a spot the width of a hand

below the first cut. As they worked their way around the tree men with adzes hacked out the loosened chips. Day after day they toiled, with the waist-like scarf growing deeper. Finally the tree gave a little shiver, and a cry of warning went up.

After running to a safe distance down the gorge the panting tree-fellers turned to watch. An occasional creak or groan came from the cut, but the tree still stood.

"Puh, we'll have to do a lot more cutting before it falls," Pararaka scoffed. "Come on!"

"Stay where you are!" ordered Apiroa, who was in charge of the work. The minutes dragged by, and Pararaka was starting to taunt his mates with cowardice when a gust of wind swirled down the gorge. This time a sharp crack came from the base of the tree, followed by a loud groaning noise. Slowly and ponderously the huge, spreading head of branches started to move across the sky.

A loud rushing noise, like that of a heavy squall of wind, sounded as the tree toppled. Smaller trees in its path were smashed like kindling sticks, and the ground shook underfoot as the forest giant crashed to earth. Rehua hurried forward, his lined face taut with anxiety. Had the trunk cracked when it fell? He scrambled over the tangle of smashed limbs, but there was no sign of damage anywhere on the huge log. He chanted his thanks to Tane.

Maui raced away to convey the good news to the village. When the felling gang came home Hikurangi addressed the assembled people. "You have worked hard and well. To-night we hold a feast and dance to celebrate the successful felling of the great tree."

Cries of delight greeted the announcement. Four men snatched up spears and clubs, then ran off to round up and kill pigs for the banquet. The boys carried home big bundles of firewood. Most of the girls hurried into the forest to gather flowers; Kura, Hina, and Ngaio picked up some small, boat-shaped wooden dishes and pearl-shell scrapers with notched edges.

At the coconut grove they husked ripe nuts by striking them on a pointed stake set in the ground. The shells were then broken open, the white meat in them was scraped to shreds with the notched shells and placed in the dishes. These were stood in the sun, with clam shells under the holes in their lower ends to catch the oil as it dripped out.

Among the beautiful breadfruit-trees was the open-air marae temple, floored with slabs of basalt worn smooth by many generations of bare feet and surrounded by a raised tier of dressed coral blocks to serve as seats. At one end two huge, grim-faced stone statues stared out to seaward. While some men swept away the dead leaves which littered the dancing-floor others erected the poles on which the flower, fern, and feather decorations would be hung.

That night, under the light of the full moon, flower-decked girls, their satiny skins gleaming with coconut oil, swayed and stepped through the figures of the traditional dances, while sharkskin drums throbbed and boomed to give the time to the twinkling feet and quivering bodies.

When the girls were weary lines of young men took their place. Not until the moon was sinking behind the mountain did the celebration end. Every one slept late next morning, for there was no need to prepare food when piles of pork and kumara were left over from the sunset feast of the previous evening.

But on the following day they were all astir at dawn. The holiday was over, and now the work had to be resumed.

4

THE CANOE TAKES SHAPE

Several more days of work with the big chisel, wielded by the same team of men, were needed to separate the head of the tree from the trunk. Then Rehua and Apiroa rubbed a mixture of oil and charcoal on a thin string and stretched it along the top of the great log from end to end.

"Go to the middle of this line, Maui; lift it up and let it go," Rehua directed. Maui obeyed; when he released the cord it left a black mark down the centre of the trunk. With this as a base-line Rehua laid out the shape of the hull.

"Start the men on the work of cutting out," he said to Apiroa. "Watch that none go beyond my marks."

The men lined up on either side and began to peck away with their adzes. Old men squatted near by, with slabs of stone, sand, water, and boy assistants, ready to sharpen the tools as they grew blunt.

Rehua walked around for a time, watching the work, then he sat down to wait until Apiroa needed his advice. Maui joined the old canoe chief.

"Last night I listened outside the council house. I heard you speak of legends unknown to my people," the boy said. "Can you tell me where we came from?"

"Our original Hawaiki lies far away over there," Rehua replied, pointing to the north-west. "It was called Aitia-te-Varinga-Nui."

"The Great Land of Aitia, where food grew in mud," Maui echoed. "That'd be taro, I guess."

"No. Vari was a different kind of food. It had thin stems.

On top of them grew small brown seeds. The people gathered them, ground them up between stones, moistened the powder with water, made it into cakes, and cooked it. In that land our ancestors lived in stone houses."

Maui tried to imagine what such structures would be like. You could build walls of coral blocks, like those around the marae, but how could you make a roof of rocks? Rehua couldn't answer that point.

"And did the people sail away from this land of Aitia because too many lived there, as is the case on this island?" Maui inquired.

"They left because they were driven out. During the time when Nga-Taito-Ariki was high chief a strange people from the north invaded the land. They were as a shoal of little fish for numbers. With bows they shot arrows having feathers at one end and a sharp stone point on the other.

"Our people couldn't fight against them. They kept out of spear range and shot down our warriors with their arrows. The high chief saw there was only one thing to do. The people must sail away and find a new land, leaving these invaders in possession of the old one."

Rehua went on to relate the story of the first of the Polynesian migrations. The canoes were supplied with food and water. Pigs, dogs, and fowls were put aboard, as well as rooted cuttings and seeds of fruit-trees and vegetables, then they set off. Many craft were never heard of again, but others found uninhabited islands far away to the south-east, and there new settlements were established.

"They had to choose islands," Rehua pointed out. "On the mainlands lived many savages with dark skins. A canoe carries only twenty warriors. How could so small a force take a country from the thousands already in possession?"

For many generations the people lived on those islands, but the population increased until some had to go off again to find new homes. They found big islands to the eastward, but on these were more savages who shot long arrows at anyone who tried to land. The voyagers were able to find small uninhabited islands far out in the sea, however, and they settled on them. At this point in his story Rehua looked at his young companion.

"You know how a canoe chief locates an island without being able to see it, Maui?"

"He watches the direction taken by sea-birds when they fly out from it at dawn to feed, or when they fly home again to it in the afternoon."

"Yes. On these small islands the people gave up growing the vari food in mud, for they could use the breadfruit-tree instead. Wherever they went after that they took this tree with them. Many children were born, so more people sailed on to new lands.

"There was also trouble among the people. No longer did one great chief rule them. There were many small chiefs, who were jealous of each other. Some went to war against neighbouring islands."

"Like the men of Oropana attacking your island?" Maui suggested.

"Yes. Men who long to slay others. Your Pararaka, who wanted to kill me, seems such a one."

"He's not fit to be a chief!" Maui said contemptuously.

"No—but such men can usually find others willing to follow them. Well, as I was saying, there was war among the people of those islands. Survivors among those defeated in battle had to jump into their canoes and sail off, to save their lives. These also colonized new islands. And so our people have moved from island to island, until they came to this great Ocean-of-Kiwa, where we have lived ever since."

Maui was enthralled by this history of his people. Now his island would be carrying it on by sending off voyagers in search of yet another homeland. But would they always be able to find uninhabited islands as the old ones grew overcrowded? Perhaps Rehua would know.

"Does the world go on for ever, Chief, or is there an end to it?"

"It has an end. Many years ago a great canoe chief, Ui-te-Rangiora, sailed south in his canoe *Te-Ivi-O-Atea* to see what lay there. Day after day passed. The air grew colder and the waves became larger. They came to a strange, dark, misty place, not seen by the sun.

"There they saw islands which floated on the sea. They were white, like scraped arrowroot. No trees or grass grew on them. The canoe sailed up to the lee of one and found it was made of a cold white rock. The men broke off pieces, meaning to take them home, but the rock turned to water as it lay in the canoe!"

Maui found this hard to believe. A rock which turned to water! But old Rehua seemed quite positive about it—and it would never do to voice your doubts. So the world ended in a realm of cold and storms? Rehua interrupted the boy's wandering thoughts.

"Come. It is time to inspect the work of the adze-men."

Down in the village food for the midday meal of the

canoe-makers had been packed. The women looked around
for the girls who were to carry the baskets up to the head
of the valley.

"What's this?" snapped Hina's mother. "You must first
comb your hair and put on a clean skirt? The men can go
hungry while you make yourself pretty? If you're not on
your way before I count ten..." Hina grabbed up the
heavy basket and fled. Kura and Ngaio followed her. Hina
stopped as soon as they were out of sight of anyone in the
village.

"I won't go up there looking a fright!" she said obstinately, dumping the basket by the side of the path and
taking a comb from the waistband of her skirt. "Be a dar-
ling, Kura. Part my hair nicely for me, then I'll do yours."

"Where do I come in?" Ngaio complained.

"We'll do yours presently. Hunt around for some
flowers while you're waiting."

"But there's none here. They were all picked for the
dance!"

"Go on ahead till you find some, then. I'll do your hair
when we catch up."

Before they entered the gorge the girls stopped to look
at the reflections of their flower-wreathed heads and necks
in a still creek pool. After combing out the strands of their
bark skirts with their fingers they walked on, hips swaying
and faces ready to break into smiles. It was all wasted
effort.

The men were waiting at a spot where a bend in the
track hid the fallen tree from view, for it was tapu for
women to go near a canoe under construction. They did
not look at the girls; they had eyes only for the food-
baskets.

"What kept you so long?" Apiroa growled, after he had
unwrapped a package of cooked fish and had shared it out.

"It's a long way—and the baskets get heavy when you
carry them uphill," Hina protested. She watched the men,

ready to return a smile, but they gave all their attention to the food.

As they walked home with the empty baskets she said petulantly, "Men make me tired. All they think of is eating!"

"Next time we mustn't be late with their dinners," Ngaio suggested. "Perhaps they'll look at us then."

As they neared the village she stripped off her flower garlands, threw them over a bush, and disarranged her hair. The other girls copied her example. A moment later Hikurangi came into view, walking up to see how the work was progressing. They stood aside respectfully to let him pass.

"That was a narrow escape, if you like!" Hina giggled, when the old chief was out of hearing.

Hikurangi returned in the middle of the afternoon. When he came to the spot where the girls had halted he paused to study their footmarks, looked over the bush, and saw the discarded flower garlands. His face twitched with amusement, then he picked up the six wreaths.

When he reached the village he walked into the house where the girls were weaving leaf platters for the evening meal. Assuming a ferocious scowl, he handed to each a couple of garlands and walked out without speaking. Kura, Ngaio, and Hina stared at one another.

"What does this mean?" said Hina's mother. The old chief's back had been towards her, and she hadn't seen the expression on his face.

"Just little gifts to show how he appreciates the way we're working," her quick-witted daughter replied, smiling innocently.

Day after day the team of men chipped away at the light yet close-grained wood of the huge log; deeper grew the layer of chips underfoot. Gradually the outside of the hull took shape. Rehua now watched all the time, sighting along the sides to check the lines. Where a bulge was being left he rubbed the area with charcoal as a guide to the man working on that section.

One morning he stared at where Pararaka had been chopping, then rounded on him. "You have cut too deep! Here's a hollow!"

"I can't see it," the young man said obstinately.

Apiroa came along to have a look. "Yes, you've gone too far!" he agreed. "Put that adze down. From now on you can help widen the track to the beach. I've given you two warnings about careless work. I'm not overlooking it this time."

His face dark with humiliation and rage, Pararaka flung down the adze and went off to do labouring work.

After the outside of the hull had been shaped the wood was rubbed with shark oil to prevent it from cracking through drying out too quickly, then the men started on the far more arduous task of hollowing the inside. Rehua watched the work anxiously, for a mistake now could ruin everything. Maui followed him, carrying the measuring-sticks and the charcoal for marking. His friend Hauka was kept busy on scraping up the chips and tossing them over the side.

One day, after Kura had handed over her basket of food, she caught Maui's glance and signed to him to come out of hearing of the others.

"Is it true that a few boys will be allowed to go?" she said anxiously.

"That's what they're saying."

"Will you be one?"

"I hope so!" His face was full of eagerness.

Kura's big, dark eyes looked into his, then her gaze went to the ground. With her toe she brushed away some dead leaves. Maui saw her mouth quiver, then realization came.

"You'd like to go?" he said softly.

"If you do," she admitted, then she snatched up the empty basket and fled.

Maui stared after her until Hauka called to him. "All the lobster meat'll be gone if you don't grab your share pretty quickly!"

Maui was very thoughtful during the rest of the day. That evening he waited for a chance to speak to Kura without being overheard. "If I tell you something you'll promise not to repeat it?"

"Yes," she said breathlessly.

"Not even to Hina or Ngaio?"

"I promise. Tell me, quick!"

"Rehua said it to Hikurangi. 'If we send two or three boys off, girls for them to marry when they grow up must go too.' You're bound to be chosen."

Kura felt her cheeks grow hot with pride, then a sudden doubt made her catch her breath. What if Maui himself wasn't included? I won't go if he's left, she decided.

Thereafter, whenever Kura's mother wanted her to carry out an additional task, she always knew where to find her. The girl would be sitting in a corner of the house, stencilling designs on tapa or scraping ribbons of hibiscus bark for a skirt.

"Just things to go with the canoe," was her explanation. She did not divulge her secret hope to accompany them.

Rehua grew very critical as the hollowing of the canoe hull drew near completion. More and more adze-men were sent to join those who were widening the path to the coast. The last delicate adze-strokes were left to Apiroa and his two best assistants.

Then the stems of banana plants were carried up and laid on the track to make a slippery skidway. The two stout hauling ropes were fastened to the hull. All the men went up the valley to take part in the karakia ceremony in which the canoe said farewell to the stump on which it had grown for centuries.

Uropaki led the solemn chanting, wearing his best feather headdress and his ceremonial robe of tapa. When the service was over he took them off, handed them to an old man for safe keeping, and moved to a rope to do his share of the hauling.

As soon as the men chosen for the task were in position Hikurangi raised his walking-staff and gave the order to heave.

5

THE LAUNCHING OF THE "TERE-MOANA"

Facing the canoe, heels dug into the soft soil, the two lines of men gripped the ropes and struck up the canoe-hauling song:

> "*He* kimihanga!
> *He* torohanga!
> *He* kiteatanga!
> *He* openga!"

With every beat of the ancient chant—it was so old that the meaning of the words had been forgotten—the bodies of the haulers swayed, their muscles bulging with the effort, and the canoe jerked forward. A day of heavy labour brought the hull to the beach, where it was laid upon wooden skids, and a long, thatched shed was built over it to protect the wood from the sun.

"It would have been better to have built a canoe with twin hulls," Rehua remarked to Maui, when the topside planking and the outrigger booms were being fitted. "There is room for the crew to move about on the platform which connects them. Such a canoe sails faster, too.

"There is also more room inside the hulls for the storage of food and water. But your island had only this one great tree on it, so we had no choice. This single-hulled one should be a fine craft, all the same."

Every family offered its most cherished possessions to equip the emigrants. Rehua examined the proffered gifts with a critical eye, rejecting some and accepting others. Kura brought him the fine mat on which she had spent all her spare time for the past year.

"That will certainly be included," he assured her.

As the launching day drew near the people wondered who would be chosen to complete the crew. Some men and their wives were bound to be selected. First came Ruapara and Utea. They had been Uropaki's best pupils in the House of Learning. In their memories were stored the legends, myths, songs, and genealogies of the tribe. They were now raised to the status of Tohunga priests.

There were also two men skilled at gardening, two who had shown great skill at woodworking, and three expert fishermen, but only Rehua and Hikurangi knew the names of the rest. Pararaka was quite sure that he had been chosen.

"Who is stronger than I, or a better fighter?" he bragged. "They can't leave me out!"

Then came the morning when old Rehua, after a final inspection, returned to the village wearing a happy smile. "It is finished," he announced. "The tapu has been lifted. You may look at it now."

Chattering excitedly, the women and girls dropped their work and hurried along the beach to the canoe-house. They gazed up at the low figurehead, its beaked face looking ahead to enable the canoe to see where it was going, then at the high and beautifully carved stern-piece.

It had taken months of weary work to build it—but what a fine craft it was! The size of it! Why, you could walk under the big, curved booms which carried the huge outrigger float!

Children were lifted on the shoulders of parents to enable them to look into the hull. Boys scrambled around on it, pretending to be sailing to a new land. The older people felt an uplifting of their hearts. Such a fine craft should carry its crew safely to a new homeland!

Lately it had seemed as though the work on the canoe would go on for ever, with never any time to rest except when asleep. But now it was finished at last. There would again be time for dancing, singing, swimming, and gathering flowers.

Presently Rehua struck his staff against a post of the canoe-house to gain attention. He directed the women to prepare flower garlands for decorating the craft and told the men to place the carrying poles under the hull.

"Our great canoe will be launched as soon as the tide comes in," he added.

The women and girls ran off to gather the flowers, and the men completed the preparations for launching. That afternoon every able-bodied man stooped to grip one of the carrying poles and lifted at the word of command. Shoulder-high they bore her down the beach and lowered her into the water.

Baptizing her was a very solemn ceremony. Every man who had helped with her construction now rocked her until she had 'swallowed seawater' by shipping some over the bow and stern; then Uropaki, facing the direction of the distant land to which she would sail, named her *Tere-Moana* and besought Tangaroa, God of the Ocean, to grant her a safe, swift voyage.

After this the mast was stepped and stayed, the big sail,

stiffened like a fan with long, thin poles, was put aboard, and she was loaded with enough rock ballast to be the equivalent of a cargo. Finally thirty men scrambled over the gunwales to serve as the crew on her trial cruise.

The crowd on the beach watched her being paddled around the bay for a time, with Rehua and Hikurangi standing beside the steersman on the stern platform, then she headed for the reef entrance. As soon as she was clear of the coral the sail crept up the mast and she headed out to sea.

When she returned and the anchor stone had been dropped the crew waded ashore. Rehua wore a proud smile. "I have handled several great outrigger canoes, and I have seen many of them," he told the people, "but none have been better than yours."

That evening there was a feast to celebrate the launching. When it was over Hikurangi called for attention. "Here are those chosen to seek a new homeland in Aotearoa," he said solemnly. Maui listened to the names with his heart hammering; Kura was pale and trembling.

"Four young people will accompany them," the high chief added. "They are Maui and Hauka, Kura and Ngaio."

The silence which followed was broken by a cry of dismay from a woman. "My baby! I can't go without her!"

"A young child can't be taken on a long voyage," her husband pointed out, his own voice husky with grief.

"I'll look after the little one," said the woman's mother. "You'll soon have another. They come quickly enough at your age." But the young woman refused to be comforted.

Then the gathering was startled by an angry roar from Pararaka. He had boasted that he was sure to be chosen, and being omitted was a dreadful blow to his mana prestige. What made it worse was the fact that nobody seemed surprised because he was left out.

"I shall go!" he shouted, addressing the high chief while standing—a serious breach of etiquette. "I have the right to be included! Did I not help to fell the great tree and build the canoe? Who pulled harder on the hauling ropes? Am I not the best warrior on the island?"

Hikurangi ordered him to be quiet, but Pararaka, spitting with rage, continued to shout. The high chief turned to two of the men whose rank entitled them to sit beside him. "Take that ill-mannered fool away!" he directed.

Before the two lesser chiefs could move Pararaka snatched up his club and bounded through the crowd. He seized Hikurangi by his white hair; instantly Maui sprang up, grabbed the head of the club as Pararaka swung it over his shoulder to strike, and hung on like an octopus.

A savage jab in the face from Pararaka's elbow made him dizzy with pain, but he did not release his grip. Then there was a loud thump, and the weapon came free in his hands. Through the tears which streamed from his eyes he saw Pararaka lying senseless on the ground and a man standing over him with another club in his hands.

"Take him away and tie him to a tree," Hikurangi gasped.

The unconscious man was dragged off, and the chiefs went to the council house to discuss the deplorable affair. The crowd broke up, wondering what punishment would be inflicted on a man who had dared to lay hands on the tapu person of their leader.

Pararaka recovered his senses half an hour later. His mother, weeping at the humiliation which had been brought on her family, was allowed to wash the clotted blood from his head and face and to bring him a drink of coconut water, but not until dawn did he learn his fate. Then four grim-faced men, clubs in their hands, came up. One slipped the noosed end of a rope over his head, he was untied and led to the beach.

Here he saw an old one-man canoe, containing a dozen ripe coconuts, a couple of fishing-lines, a paddle, bailer, and an adze. Uropaki stood beside it.

"For disputing the orders of our high chief you are to be sent away," said the priest. "Get into this canoe and go! When you laid hands on the sacred person of Hikurangi you broke a tapu. For that the gods will inflict their own punishment."

Pararaka glanced around and realized the enormity of his offence. Not one person was there to bid him farewell! "Your father and mother hide their heads for the shame you've brought on them!" Uropaki explained.

The condemned man gulped, feeling lonely and miserable. Then he jerked up his head defiantly. These people had never valued his great strength. What opportunities were there for a warrior on this island? In some other land they'd appreciate him!

The man who held the rope stood ready to haul the noose tight if Pararaka showed fight, but there was no need for it. Without a backward glance the outcast pushed off the canoe, squatted in it, and took up the paddle. The loose end of the rope was tossed after him.

Pararaka slipped the noose over his head and coiled the rope. It might be useful, he thought, as he laid it in the bottom of the canoe and paddled towards the gap in the reef. Before long he was a speck in the distance. At sunset the man who had gone to the top of the mountain to watch came back to report: "He is now out of sight."

Next day the people made the final preparations. Clam and octopus meat was hung on lines to dry; taro and plantains were baked, then dried until they resembled chips of wood.

Poi breadfruit paste was dried and wrapped. Bottle-shaped hue gourds which had ripened on the vines were cleaned inside, ready to be filled with water. A big number of ripe coconuts were husked and placed aboard. A

large fishing-net was made for the voyagers to take with
them; there were bundles of the best tapa cloth, a stack of
weapons and every woodworker donated his best adzes
and chisels.

There was a long debate as to whether pigs should be
taken as part of the livestock, but Rehua opposed it. "There
is plenty of meat in Aotearoa," he said. "One of those great
moa birds will feed many people." It was decided to take
only a crate of fowls, a cage containing some of the vegetarian kiore rats, and a couple of bitches which were going
to have pups.

To plant in the gardens in the new land there were
rooted slips of breadfruit and aute paper mulberry, banana
and plantain, as well as sprouting coconuts and many
leaf-wrapped packages of seeds. All were placed under the
steering platform in the stern of the canoe, where there
was least risk of damage by sea water.

The rest of the gear was stacked under the decking in
the bow, behind the supplies of food and water. When the
farewell feast was being prepared Rehua took Maui with
him while he made a final inspection of the canoe.

Every lashing was given a close scrutiny. He tested the
soundness of the cords on which the scoop-like wooden
bailers were hung. He counted the paddles tied along the
sides just below the gunwales, checked the beckets in
which the great steering paddle was slung and examined
the spare coils of rope.

"These are the duties of a canoe chief," Rehua told
Maui. "No matter how careful every one else has been, you
must never take it for granted that all is well. Yours is the
final responsibility."

That evening, as he ate his share of the final feast, Maui
found himself viewing the impending departure with
mixed feelings. He and Hauka had been paid a great com-
pliment by being selected from more than forty boys. He
longed to be off—yet whenever he thought of leaving his

D

family and friends his eyes became hot and his throat grew hard and lumpy, making it difficult to swallow.

He found it was affecting Kura in the same way. "If only one could go, yet stay at the same time," she whispered; then added, "How silly it sounds when you try to put it into words!"

"I know what you mean," he assured her.

Presently Maui's father told him to go to their house and lie down. "You must get some sleep. To-morrow will be a hard day," he warned, then looked up at the stars. "Nearly half the night has gone now."

Maui was sure that he wouldn't be able to sleep, but he lay on his mats. For a long time he listened to the voices of the people at the marae and watched the reflected light of the temple fires flickering on the thatch overhead. This was his last night in the home where he had been born and reared. . . .

He fell into an uneasy doze which seemed to last only a few moments, then he opened his eyes to find the house lit by a candlenut torch and people stirring around him. His mother handed him a piece of pork and a couple of baked plantains which she had saved from the feast.

"You mustn't go off hungry. No food will be issued on board till sunset," she said.

Maui found it hard to eat. He felt like telling them to go without him. As if she had read his thoughts, his mother put her arms around him. Her tears fell warmly on his face.

"You marry Kura when you grow up," she whispered. "She's not as pretty as Ngaio, but she'll be a better wife."

"May you grow to be a strong, brave man," said his father, handing him a bowl of water. "Swallow it all—you won't get another drink till nightfall." He glanced at the palm-leaf torches moving along the beach. "It is time to go."

Maui picked up the little basket which held the parting

gifts of his family and friends; fish-hooks inlaid with pearl-shell, a hair-comb, drinking-bowl, an adze, and a set of chisels. It felt heavier than it had been when he had handled it last; he felt inside it, and his fingers found some ripe bananas. His mother hadn't eaten her share of the fruit at the feast, he saw, but had kept it for him. There was also an extra gourd of water.

His family were silent when they accompanied him to the beach. After a final hug all round he waded out to the *Tere-Moana*, and a man helped him to climb aboard. "Stay by the mast to be out of the way," he directed. Hauka was there, Maui found, with the two girls crouching at his feet crying bitterly.

"To think you'll never see your parents or sisters again!" Kura sobbed.

"Why didn't they let Hina come too?" Ngaio wailed.

6

DOWN THE ARA-MOANA SEA-PATH

By the time the light was broad enough for faces to be recognized, the bustle of stowing personal belongings was over and the thirty men and women who formed the crew were unlashing their paddles. A fishing-canoe passed slowly along the side of the big craft, with Hikurangi standing in it to bid each one a personal farewell.

When he came to Maui he held out something which made the boy gasp. It was the old man's beautifully carved club. "You saved me when Pararaka attacked me," Hikurangi explained. "This is a chief's weapon. When you grow up I hope you will be a leader!"

Maui, his eyes wild with surprise and delight, stowed it away carefully. Two men, standing on the bow decking, hauled up the big anchor stone. Others assisted to lower it to the bottom grating, where they coiled the rope around it neatly.

"Paddle!" Rehua ordered, standing beside the steersman at the stern. He gave the time by tapping his walking-staff on the platform. A wail of grief came from the crowd on the beach. The voice of Uropaki rose above it.

"This is no way to part from loved ones! Sing the hymn of farewell instead of weeping!"

At first haltingly, then gaining strength, the song rang across the ever-widening gap between canoe and shore. Maui, gazing at the golden sunrise with tear-dimmed eyes, seemed to hear an echo to the words in his heart:

"Good-bye, our loved ones,
Our hearts are heavy,
Fast fall our tears,
We won't forget you!

May Hine-Moana,
The Maid of the Ocean,
Be your sure guide
Across the wide sea."

The paddles moved faster as the beat of Rehua's staff quickened. Fainter grew the singing behind them; louder the crash and rumble of the surf as the canoe neared the gap in the reef. Sunrise was flushing on the mountain summit when the *Tere-Moana* began to pitch in the swells of the open sea.

"Cease paddling! Set the sail!" said Rehua.

A dozen pairs of hands unlashed the great roll of matting. It slatted and rustled as its peak was hoisted to the masthead, then it bellied to the press of the breeze as the sheet-rope was belayed. The canoe started to surge through the water. Maui began to forget his sorrow as he watched the behaviour of the craft under sail.

Roller after roller swept up from astern to tower over the steersman. Just as you feared the crest would break and swamp the craft the stern would lift, and the wave would slide under the keel.

Rehua stepped down from the steering platform and made a tour of inspection, seeing that all paddles were in place and lashed securely, then he sat on the bottom grating in the bows, with the anchor stone as a back-rest.

Maui looked back at the island which had been his home. Already the whole of it could be seen, with the surf leaping at the foot of its reddish-brown cliffs and the forest-clad ridges rising to the craggy central peak. Presently Kura stood up, dried her tear-wet cheeks with her long, dark hair, and gazed in the same direction.

"I've often wondered what it looked like from the sea," she remarked. "As it's tapu for a girl to enter a fishing-canoe, this is my first view of it."

Every one except the steersman, the look-out man, and old Rehua kept their gaze on their Hawaiki island home-land. Gradually its size dwindled, and the green of the tree-clad slopes began to take on the blue tinge of distance.

When it was far astern Rehua stood up and called the two boys.

"Make this your first lesson in finding your way to a far-off land," he said. "See that little cloud forming on the lee side of the mountain? See how it hangs there when all the other clouds drift across the sky? You look for such a cloud when seeking an island."

He pointed to the flocks of terns and boobies, with an occasional frigate-bird, which followed the canoe. "Those are the land birds. Some day you may be looking eagerly for them, as a sign that land is no more than a day's sail away."

The wind thrummed and shrilled through the stays, the canoe's bows flung rainbow-shot fans of spray as she pitched, and a school of porpoises kept pace with the craft, arching their grey bodies out of the water as they rose to take snorting breaths.

Slowly the lower portions of the island sank out of sight over the rim of the world. When the sun was almost directly overhead only a small black speck was visible at one end of a banner of white cloud.

The last glimpse of their Hawaiki seemed to quiver on the horizon for a little time; then it vanished and was seen no more. Only the Ao-Motu land cloud was still visible as a dwindling white patch where sea and sky met. When it had nearly faded from view Rehua pointed to it, then to a few distant land birds which were now flying homeward to roost for the night on the island's cliffs.

"That is all you see when you first make a landfall—but it is enough to guide a canoe chief," he told them.

Late in the afternoon a meal was served from the baskets of fresh food which had been put aboard at the last moment. The four young people shared the water in a green coconut which Hauka had brought. The sharp edge of their grief at leaving their families and friends had dulled now. Hauka tried to talk cheerfully.

"Guess the palms we plant in Aotearoa will take a few years to grow up and bear nuts," he remarked, looking at the one from which Maui was drinking. He gave Ngaio a nudge. "Perhaps the first will be used at our wedding feast."

"What makes you so sure I'll marry you?" she retorted, with a glance of affected disdain. "Rehua says many people live in this new land. I might find a man more to my liking."

"That gives me an idea!" Hauka cried. "I won't have to take you because you're the only one in sight! I'll have lots of girls to choose from. What about you, Maui?"

"Sounds good to me," Maui agreed, then he saw the hurt expression on Kura's face and comforted her by touching her foot and smiling at her under cover of raising the drinking-nut to see if a drop of the sweet water remained in it.

Sunset glowed with the brilliant colours which forecasted fine weather. As the stars trembled into view Rehua pointed to those which would guide them on their voyage. Clear in the west shone Kopu, the evening star; low in the southern sky was Maahu-Tonga, the Southern Cross. The course to be steered was Tonga-Ma-Uru, west-south-west. The old man went on to warn the crew of their duties.

"Five times during the darkness you will relieve the man at the steering paddle and the one who keeps the look-out ahead, for arms and eyes grow tired if kept working too long. Every one must watch the lashings to see that none work loose. The women will keep the canoe bailed out."

Those not on duty wrapped themselves in sleeping-mats, for the wind was cold now the sun had gone. The canoe was too crowded for the people to stretch out on the bottom gratings, but by huddling together they found sitting room for every one. Here and there somebody cried softly, thinking of loved ones left behind.

Rehua sat by the anchor stone, dozing at intervals. Whenever he awakened he glanced at the stars to see that the correct course was being steered, then listened to the noise of the wind in the stays, the creaking of the mast, and the slap and rush of the seas. Any change in those sounds would warn him that something was amiss.

When Maui awakened in the morning, chilled and cramped, he thought for a moment that it must be all a dream, for he could hear the familiar crowing of roosters. Then he realized that it came from the poultry coop in the stern. Shivering, he stood up to look around.

As the light grew it revealed a cold-looking, grey sea, empty except for an occasional flying-fish skipping and gliding over the rollers. Not a sea-bird was in sight. Other people began to stir, and Rehua found tasks for all.

The dogs were untied and allowed to run about on the grating for exercise. The fowls and rats were fed on scraped coconut meat. Two trolling-lines were streamed astern in the hope of hooking a big fish. Some of the women soaked the dried meat and vegetables for the morning meal. Others raised the sections of grating and bailed out the water which had leaked through the seams between the dug-out hull and the topside planking. Two men inspected every lashing on the craft.

The gardeners crawled under the stern platform with a gourd of water and let a little of it drip on the earth and fibre packing around the roots of the plants. Sleeping-mats were rolled up and tied below the gunwales to get them out of the way. Faces were washed with sea water and, when the wind had dried the skin, were rubbed with coconut oil.

The morning meal was eaten when the sun was high in the sky, but there was no allowance of drinking-water with it. Maui took the gourd from his basket and shared a mouthful apiece with Kura, Ngaio, and Hauka.

For six days the canoe sailed steadily along the Ara-Moana sea-path, then came a morning when the breeze died to fitful flaws of wind, and a haze of streaky, storm-warning clouds spread across the sky from the north. The sea rose in heavy, lumpy swells.

Rehua was filled with anxiety as he read the weather signs. The gods must be angry, although all the omens had been favourable when the voyage began. "Take in the sail and lower the mast," he ordered. "Four of you use paddles to keep the canoe head to sea. Two of you bring the spare spar to the bows."

The men scrambled to obey. Overhead the haze thickened fast, and a few ragged wisps of scud went tumbling across the sky, forerunners of a heavy bank of cloud. A bridle was put on the spar to make it float broadside on, the stoutest rope was hitched to it, and it was dropped overboard to act as a sea anchor which would keep the *Tere-Moana* facing the wind.

The great cloud-bank, as solid in appearance as a cliff and with jagged lightning flashes darting across its face, swept down on them. With it came the wind, roaring and booming as it swept sheets of stinging spray from the wave-crests. Soon the canoe was battling with heavier seas than even Rehua had ever seen.

The two priests chanted prayers in which they begged Tangaroa to spare them. The women, their hair hanging in wet strings, bailed unceasingly to keep down the water which came aboard as spray or squirted through the seams.

The roaring gusts grew stronger. Some of the men took a turn at the bailing to give the panting women a chance to rest. The wooden scoops had to be gripped tightly to prevent the wind from wrenching them out of their hands. The rest of the men scrambled about, putting on extra lashings when they saw anything starting to give way.

Night came down, soot-dark except for the ghostly gleam of breaking seas. The wind seemed to redouble its fury. High overhead could be heard the wild, exultant screams of the atua spirits as they rode the wings of the storm and mocked the despairing efforts of the crew. Finally, when even the stoutest hearts were abandoning hope, the eastern sky began to lighten and the wind started to drop.

By midday it was no more than a strong breeze, and the *Tere-Moana* was under sail again. The exhausted crew were able to sleep in turns. But sunset was not the fine-weather one for which Rehua had been hoping. The red in it looked sullen and forbidding. During the night the breeze was so light that the canoe barely kept steerage-way. Morning dawned upon a flat calm.

All through the day Rehua looked in vain for signs of wind. With a heavy heart he realized that they might be encountering one of those deadly, windless spells of hot

weather, following a big storm, of which such terrible
stories were told in the legends of canoe voyages.

The sun blazed down, reflected from the oily sea in
flashes which made the eyes burn and ache. The panting
dogs had to be allowed to lie on the steering platform; the
cages holding the rats and fowls were hung over the side
to get the shade cast by the limp sail.

The crew could not rest by lying on the bottom gratings,
for down in the hull the heat was suffocating. A few at a
time could stretch out on the steering platform and on the
decking in the bows, but the rest had to stand about, bailing sea water over their bodies in an effort to keep cool.
The man at the steering paddle used it like an oar to keep
the canoe stern-on to the waves.

They longed for the darkness to come and give them a
chance to rest, but at dusk Rehua shattered their hopes.
"You must paddle all night!" he ordered. He frowned
angrily when cries of protest replied.

"Other canoe chiefs have met with calms such as this,"
he told them. "If we wait for wind, as some of you suggest,
we may drift about till we die of thirst." He pointed to the

south-west. "Down there the winds are blowing. We must reach them before all our drinking-water is used."

The crew unlashed the paddles and took up their positions, with the four young people using spare ones. All through the night, with an occasional pause for a brief rest, they laboured at the paddles, keeping time to the *tap-tap-tap-TAP!* . . . *tap-tap-tap-TAP!* of Rehua's staff. When the dawn came they rigged matts to serve as an awning, ate a meal, drank a scanty allowance of water, then sank into what was more an exhausted stupor than a sleep.

Day after day the calm continued; night after night they paddled the heavy canoe. On the fourth day, in spite of their care, the drooping fowls began to die. The birds lay on the floor of their coop with wings slack and gaping beaks. Every little while one of the crew would pour sea water over them.

But it was in vain. There would be a squawk, a few flaps and kicks, then another one was dead. By the middle of the afternoon all had gone. The meat was used to feed the dogs, and the cage was dropped overboard.

Precious fresh water had to be dribbled on the roots of the plants, which were wilting in the heat. Some of the crew protested that it would be better to paddle by day and sleep at night, but Rehua was adamant.

"Working under a hot sun makes you need far more drinking-water than if you paddle at night," he told them. In an effort to keep up their strength he began to issue the ripe coconuts which formed their emergency supply of food and drink, but still there was no end to the terrible calm and the baking heat.

The crew now bore little resemblance to the band of healthy, strong young men and women who had sailed off on a great adventure. Eyes were sunken and inflamed, lips were cracked, bodies wasted, and hands blistered cruelly from the paddling. How pitifully small seemed the milk in the ripe coconuts or the allowance of water from the gourds to throats and bodies parched for moisture!

On the ninth day of the calm men and women began to collapse. By the following sunrise only four of the men were still on their feet, with Kura the only woman. Rehua looked as if he might go down at any moment, but some hidden reserve of energy seemed to keep him going.

As the daylight came the haggard old man clambered on to an outrigger boom, gripped a mast stay for support, and stared towards the south-west. His eyes were so inflamed that it was difficult to see, but down there the sky did seem darker in colour, and he thought he could make out the white summits of wind-clouds on the horizon.

He counted the water-gourds which still remained in the racks. They were alarmingly few, but a further risk must be taken. He used the contents of one to soak some dry food. When the people still able to paddle had eaten, he shared another container of water among them. After allowing them to sleep for a time he shook them awake and pointed to the south-west.

"Wind-clouds are in sight," he gasped. "If we reach them we're saved." He staggered aft to steer as the four men and the girl began to paddle. He watched the bubbles on the water; how slowly they drifted past! Those five people were hardly moving the canoe. . . .

What had they done to incur the wrath of the gods? All the proper ceremonies had been observed and prayers said. His mana was still strong when he landed on the island. The building of this big craft was proof of that. Yet they had encountered the longest and worst calm of which he had ever heard!

Without ceasing to paddle and his voice little more than a croak, Ruapara the priest began to chant another prayer. Rehua felt a stirring of hope as he listened. Perhaps the gods would now relent. . . .

7

THE END OF THE VOYAGE

All through the stifling heat of the morning those five people toiled at the paddles. Whenever they had to rest for a time Rehua went into the body of the canoe and gave a sip of water apiece to the other members of the crew, to keep them alive.

All around them the horizon was ringed with an ever-changing mirage, except in the south-west, where it was not only clear but a few undoubted cloud summits could now be seen. Three men revived and helped with the paddling, then two more. Rehua looked at the dogs and rats. He decided to give the animals one more drink and moisten the roots of the plants again, but if a breeze did not come by nightfall all would have to be sacrificed.

He had just completed the watering when there was a chorus of hoarse but joyful cries and the sail boomed taut. He crawled out from beneath the stern platform to see Ruapara taking the steering paddle. Around the canoe a puff of wind was ruffling the sea.

It soon died away, but ahead they could see other patches of wind-darkened water. The gasping paddlers were stirred to a last burst of energy. Each time the sail caught a gust they held their breaths with anxiety; when the sail went limp they paddled again. At last came a puff of wind which grew stronger instead of dying away. What a relief to have a cool breeze on their parched skins; how musical was the sound of water rippling under the bows and gurgling past the sides!

Although he was giddy with exhaustion, Ruapara

remained at the helm. One by one the people who had been paddling slumped into the bottom of the canoe. Rehua sat on the fore-decking and kept a look-out ahead. The sun set, then there was a cry from aft. The old chief turned to see Ruapara staggering about on the platform.

Rehua attempted to rise and take the helm himself, but his old body was unable to meet this last demand on it. He tried to shout a warning to the crew, but his thirst-parched throat produced nothing except gasps. So this was the end, he thought sadly. Without a hand on the helm the canoe would broach and capsize. . . .

Then he saw Kura scrambling aft, ducking under booms and spreaders, treading on the prone bodies. She caught Ruapara as his knees buckled, broke his fall as he tumbled into the hull, hauled herself on to the platform, and grasped the haft of the steering paddle just in time to prevent the sail being taken by the lee.

A wave of faintness swept over Rehua. When his head cleared he found the canoe was running before a breeze which was now cold and strong. Against the darkening sky he could see Kura, feet straddled widely for balance and the wind whipping her tapa kilt and long hair.

She couldn't keep it up, he thought. Steering a big canoe was beyond the ability of a girl. But Kura had often watched the steersmen, and she now copied what she had seen them do. She eased the helm when the canoe sank into the trough of a wave; as the stern lifted and the craft scended on the crest of the following sea she brought it back on the course.

Presently the figures on the bottom of the canoe began to stir and beg for water. Rehua gave each a few mouthfuls. When the young moon was setting a man went aft to take the helm. Kura crept to where the old chief sat by the anchor stone. He groped under the stack of empty water-gourds and handed her something smooth, round, and heavy. It was the last of the green coconuts.

"You have earned it," he said, as he passed her a stone knife.

The girl hacked off the top with shaking hands. How the sweet water eased her parched throat! She lingered over each mouthful. Suddenly she paused, looked at the bodies on the gratings, handed the nut to Rehua, and went off in search of Maui. She helped him along to her vacant place, sat him with his head pillowed in the bend of her left arm, and reached for the drinking nut.

She gave him the contents a sip at a time. Once the temptation to drink herself became too strong, but after a couple of swallows she jerked the nut away from her mouth, as if ashamed of what she had done, and gave Maui the rest. Then she scraped out the soft jelly which lined the inside of the coconut and fed it to him.

"That girl will be the mother of chiefs!" Rehua said to himself, when Kura had fallen asleep with Maui's head still cradled in her arm.

With the next dawn came a stroke of luck. Ever since they had sailed from their Hawaiki, except during the great storm, the two trolling-lines had been towing astern, but no fish had taken one of the pearl-shell and feather lures which covered the wooden hooks. Now one of the lines went taut, and in the wake of the canoe they saw a great dorado leaping and splashing!

Slowly and carefully, using their arm muscles as springs to ease the strain on the line whenever the fish made a violent plunge, two of the men brought it alongside. A cord with a running noose on it was slipped down the line and hauled taut when it caught the fish's gills. Then the dorado was brought aboard.

It was killed, hacked into pieces, and every one began to chew pieces of the raw meat, swallowing the juice and spitting out the fibres. Soon another big fish was caught, followed by two small ones.

By the middle of the afternoon every one's jaws were

aching from the constant chewing, but each had swallowed a lot of plasma, free from salt, and it made a wonderful difference. They were still very weak and shaky, but no longer did parched bodies crave a drink. Ruapara chanted a hymn of gratitude to Tangaroa for the gifts of the fish from his ocean domain.

The wind grew colder as the *Tere-Moana* sailed farther south-west. The crew had to wrap themselves in many folds of tapa in order to keep some warmth in their emaciated bodies. Even the canoe itself seemed weary now: the sail was splitting, and constant bailing was needed to keep down the water which trickled through the seam between hull and topside planking, from which all the caulking had gone.

At dawn on the twenty-fifth day of the voyage Rehua heaved his stiff, aching body up on the forward outrigger boom, gripped a stay with both hands, and stared ahead, shivering as the cold wind found its way through the tapa in which he was wrapped. Sunrise gilded the wave-crests, then the grey of the ocean changed slowly to a deep and beautiful blue.

Rehua's gaze became fixed on one spot. When there could be no doubt his voice rang in a shout. Every one looked in the direction indicated by the old man's wasted arm. Far in the distance were two white specks, rising and falling as they glided over the waves. Land birds had been sighted at last!

A man helped Rehua to lower himself into the hull of the canoe, where he huddled, glad to be out of that bitter wind. Eight full water-gourds remained, the old man reflected. It would be a close thing, but they should win through now—unless something went wrong at the last moment.

The flying terns increased in numbers as the morning passed. Towards midday the look-out man sighted a long, white cloud which hung in one spot. As Hine-te-Aparinga

E

had done hundreds of years previously, he raised the triumphant cry "He Ao!" By the middle of the afternoon every one aboard could see the cloud-capped hills of Aotearoa.

Haggard faces bright with joy, the voyagers broke into cries of wonder. What a great land it was! Why, it extended as far as the eye could see, one dark blue hill rising above another. After the sun had set the land stood black against the afterglow.

Nobody slept much that night. When dawn came the land was quite close. Green slopes ran down to low cliffs, with a background of dark-blue, cloud-wreathed hills. Along the shoreline there was an occasional beach of white sand. Solemnly the two priests thanked the gods for having brought them safely down the long Ara-Moana to the great new country.

The warmth and fragrance of land met them as they sailed into a vast, island-dotted bay. Kura and Maui, standing behind the look-out man, wondered at the soft green of the grass and the deep blue of the sky. Behind them excited voices were commenting on columns of smoke in

the distance, indicating the presence of people, the flocks
of strange birds flying above the trees and the bright red
blossoms, which they found later had been named
Pohutukawa by the first arrivals, making such a brilliant
contrast to the green of the forest trees.

"Will we land here, Chief?" Maui said eagerly. "Can we
claim some of this country as ours?"

Rehua gave a regretful shake of his grey head. Those
smoke columns meant that all this part of the new land was
occupied, he explained. They might have to sail on for
days before they found country which nobody had yet
claimed. He was now seeking an island where they could
rest for a few days, renew their supplies of food and water,
and overhaul the canoe. None of the islands which they
had seen so far were large enough to have a creek or a
spring on them.

At length they sighted one which had a big hill on it and
a sandy beach on its leeward side. The sail was lowered,
and the canoe was paddled close to the shore. When he
was satisfied that the beach was bare of footprints Rehua
ordered the anchor stone to be dropped. Two men had
hauled it up when they set sail, but now they were so weak
that the combined strength of six of them was needed to
put it over the side. Slowly the canoe drifted to the full
scope of the cable, then Ruapara waded ashore to tie the
stern line to a tree.

Four men helped Rehua to the beach. Two others carried
a skinny dog apiece, and another brought the cage of rats.
A tiny creek spread over the sand at this spot, and the
people lay on its bank, alternately drinking and gazing
at the reflections of their wasted faces. The dogs lapped
greedily, and one end of the rat cage was placed in the
water, to give the little animals a drink.

Presently Rehua, who had been assisted to the shade of
a tree, gave orders. This was no time to rest and admire
the flowers. Food had to be gathered. They would find

pipi cockles in the sand of the beach and paua mutton-fish clinging to the rocks at each end of the bay. It had to be done before the tide rose. The big net must be brought ashore so they could catch fish by dragging it after sunset. All the water-gourds must be filled immediately, in case they had to leave in a hurry. . . .

Maui helped to shoot the net as soon as it was dark. Using a raft improvised from dry logs lashed together with toro vines, they paddled around in a half-circle, paying out the net as they went. When the raft returned to the shore every one helped to haul. As the bunt of the net neared the beach the trapped fish churned the water to foam.

When they hauled it up on the sand it held a flapping mass of fish whose scales gleamed in the starlight. Although every one had eaten a big meal of pipis and pauas a few hours previously, the sight of this heap of food made them hungry again. In a wooded gully, where the glow was unlikely to be seen from the mainland, they lit fires, grilled fish on the coals, and ate until they could hold no more.

"I've never tasted sweeter fish," said Ngaio.

"We won't be short of food here," Hauka remarked.

"I'm going to do some exploring as soon as we find land where nobody lives now," said Maui. "This country has very high mountains, Rehua told me. You must be able to see a long way from the top of one."

Rehua's voice came to them from the darkness beyond the fire. "We have yet to find country we can claim. You won't have time for anything but work for many, many days."

The four young people listened respectfully, but their hearts were full of happiness. Now they had arrived, what a wonderful adventure was the trip when you looked back on it! Suppose busy days did lie ahead? They wouldn't last for ever. The time would come when you could play again.

When the sleeping-mats were brought ashore, Rehua ordered six men to stay aboard, in case a squall came up in the night. The weather here was liable to sudden changes. Every man had to keep his weapons beside him, and they must take turns to keep watch. . . .

Within a week the canoe had been repaired, the sail mended, and the wasted bodies of the people were filling out. They set off with light hearts, but as they travelled along the coast they met with one disappointment after another. Every time they put into a bay, rising smoke indicated that people were in possession of the land there. Twice a crowd gathered on a beach, waving a welcome, but Rehua would not land.

"Those people have been here for generations," he explained. "As you can see, they now muster at least fifty fighting-men. If they prove treacherous and attack while we're ashore, how can our fifteen hope to win?"

But at last they came to a stretch of coast where there were no fires to be seen, and Rehua directed the helmsman to steer into a bay. It was well sheltered, and at its head they found the mouth of a river. After paddling a short distance up the stream they dropped anchor, and Rehua went ashore with a few armed men.

They found no signs of occupation except the ashes of one small fire. After Rehua had examined the ground around it he said it had been lit by some of the Tangata Whenua people, who had camped there for a night.

"They are a poor, miserable folk, who were among the first to settle here. Now they live like animals," he added. "They will cause no trouble by saying this land is theirs."

He gazed around. On the opposite side of the river a steep-sided bluff projected into the stream, with a gentle slope of land beside it. "We shall build our pa village on top of that rise," he said. "It has a narrow neck, making it easy to defend. We can make our garden on the slope alongside. The river will provide our drinking-water."

After the canoe had been moored safely in a backwater the people moved to the level summit of the bluff. It commanded a good view over the bay and the surrounding country. There were thick bushes growing there to break the wind and trees to provide shade.

Ruapara had brought ashore a small bundle wrapped in layer upon layer of scorched banana leaf. He undid it to

disclose a slab of soft white wood, a hard, thin stick, and a packet of coconut fibre. It was a special fire-making outfit which Uropaki had beseeched the gods to bless before the canoe left the Hawaiki.

Ruapara cut a groove along the slab of wood, with a hollow at one end; then he laid the gear out in the sun to warm and dry. Every one gathered a few sticks as a contribution towards the ceremonial fire.

Presently Ruapara laid the slab of wood on the ground and knelt astride it, while his wife held it steady with her foot. He rubbed the end of the stick up and down the groove, and little shavings, with some brown dust, collected in the hollow at its end. He moved the stick faster, and the shavings and dust produced became darker in

colour, while threads of smoke and a scorching smell
drifted on the air.

Now he rubbed so fast that the stick became a blur and
the smoke thickened to a cloud. Ruapara halted, with
sweat shining on his face. From the black powder in the
hollow smoke continued to rise. When he breathed on it a
red glow appeared. He tipped the spark and the shavings
into the pad of coconut fibre, waved it to and fro, and it
burst into flame. He thrust it under the heap of sticks, and
soon a fire was blazing and crackling.

Ruapara turned to survey the surrounding country, then
he raised his arms and said solemnly, "All this will be our
land as long as our fire is kept burning on it."

8

THE LAND OF LONG, BRIGHT DAYS

As soon as the ceremony of taking possession of their tribal land had been carried out, the work of home-building began. From a patch of tall scrub on the plain sounded the thudding of adzes as trees were felled for house-posts and rafters. After each pole had been cut to length women knocked the bark off it with stones and carried it to the top of the bluff. Other women hunted for the long, tough toro vines which would be used for lashings, or cut bundles of raupo reeds on the river-bank for thatch.

The two dogs scampered about happily. Rehua released the rats in a patch of forest, and the little animals soon vanished among the undergrowth. On the garden site the two experts began to clear the land which would be planted with fruit-trees and vegetables. They had already buried the sprouting coconuts in the sand above high-tide mark by the river-mouth.

"This is a wonderful place!" Maui said that evening. "No wonder it's called the Land of Long, Bright Days. They must be half as long again as they are in our Hawaiki!"

As soon as the houses had been built the colonists investigated the food resources of their tribal land. Eels, they discovered, could be speared among the reeds which lined the backwaters of the river. On any night when there was no moon it was easy to make a big haul of fish by using the dragnet on the beach. Pipi cockles could be gathered by the basketful from the sand at low tide. The rocks were thick with paua shellfish.

But they could find no wild vegetables, nor were there any native fruits except small berries of poor flavour. "We must wait until our gardens come into bearing," they told one another. The garden workers were not at all optimistic, however. The plants were growing slowly, and every few days a change in the weather would bring a cold wind to damage young, tender leaves and stems. Finally each plant was given a windbreak to shelter it.

They had thought a fence around the garden would be unnecessary, as there were no pigs here, but they had to build one to keep out the swamp hens, which did great damage by scratching at night.

The hunters started to go farther afield in search of game. Inland they came across paths made by large creatures with three toes on each foot. "Those will be the great wingless moa birds," Rehua told them.

At first they were unable to kill any, because the moas hid in the depths of forests by day, emerging after dark to feed. If tracked to their hiding-places the creatures raced away so swiftly that no man could hope to run them down. Finally a method for taking them was evolved.

Two men, armed with stout sticks of the tough manuka wood, took up a position on either side of a track along which moa birds were known to run when disturbed. Others scared the quarry towards them. The hidden men brought the great bird down by striking at its legs; then they sprang up and killed it by hitting it on the head. The meat was coarse, rank, and not to be compared with pork, but there was a lot of it on a bird. Occasionally moa eggs were found, much larger than husked coconuts.

There was also a smaller flightless bird which they named 'kiwi' on account of its peculiar cry. Its body was covered with tiny feathers, and it had a remarkably long, thin beak. The dogs helped in hunting these birds, which slept by day, and were good at finding their nests.

One day the hunters brought home a very different kind

of catch, in the form of a man and woman with unkempt hair and dirty, greasy bodies. They went naked except for a girdle of flax leaves.

"Aue! Why bring those smelly, filthy things here?" a woman objected. "What are they?"

"These are the Tangata Whenua folk I've told you about," Rehua replied.

"They'll be useful," said one of the men who had captured the pair. "They can help find food. Already they have shown us that the fern which grows everywhere has an edible root. We saw some at their camp and tried it. We found it stringy and not nearly so nice as taro and kumara, but it will serve till our crops ripen."

The two natives called themselves Maruiwi. At first it was hard to understand what they said, for they spoke a strange dialect of the Polynesian tongue, but they soon learned the language of their captors. According to their story, many generations previously their ancestors had reached this country by accident.

Some men and women in their homeland had set off in a canoe, intending to visit another island, but a great storm had driven them out to sea. They had survived by catching fish with trolling-lines. Finally, when they were almost dead from privations, the wind had drifted them to this country. Later several more canoes carrying their people had arrived in the same way.

The captives were given a small hut to sleep in, and proved to be useful, if dirty and lazy, servants.

Rehua had been waiting anxiously for a spell of weather which promised to remain fine for some time. It came at last, and he sailed away in the canoe, with a crew of eight men, to fetch pounamu stone from the west coast of the great land lying to the south of Aotearoa. Twenty-seven days later they returned, to tell a tale of sailing through a strait into a cold sea where the winds were bitter and the waves very high.

They had skirted a rocky coast and had anchored in a deep, mountain-ringed inlet. Boulders of the precious rock were found in a river which ran into it. They had brought back as many as they could find.

"You said it was green, like the water where the sea is shallow," said a man, as he helped to carry the lumps of stone up to the pa village. "These are white."

"The green colour is inside," Rehua explained.

One of the woodworkers tried to chip one stone by striking it with another, but made no impression on either.

"You must cut this stone to shape," Rehua informed him. "That is what my people did with those which I took home."

Under his direction laths of tough wood were prepared. Baskets of quartz sand were fetched from creeks in the distant hills. Two men sat down and used a strip of wood like a crosscut saw, while a third dribbled sand and water on it. Some of the grains became embedded in the wood, and gradually it made a groove.

"This is dreadfully slow work," grumbled one of the men, when a full day of sawing had worn out many strips of wood, but had done no more than make a shallow cut. "Will one live long enough to make a tool from so hard a stone?"

"It does take a long time," Rehua admitted, "but the tools made from pounamu are wonderful. Did not the men of Oropana attack my island and kill nearly all my people to get a few adzes with blades of this green stone?"

Thereafter, when any of the men had some time to spare, they took turns at the sawing. The groove in the boulder grew deeper, and finally a slab was cut off. This was sawn in halves lengthwise, and another long task began in grinding the two pieces into adze-blades. Rehua told the woodworkers to give them a far more acute edge than they did with the basalt of their homeland.

When the blades were finished they were things of great

beauty, dark green in colour and with the light showing through where the cutting edge was thin. After they had been mounted in wooden hafts every one was amazed at their cutting power. "No wonder the men of Oropana coveted such tools!" one of the woodworkers exclaimed.

Thereafter there was no more grumbling at the length of time which it took to make a blade of pounamu. Every man wanted one, and the steady rasping of stone being sawn was heard all day.

Now a strange happening drove everything else from the minds of the people. The sun was getting lower in the northern sky and the days were shortening! Every one was terrified at first. Was total darkness returning to the world, as it had been in the days before Tane separated Rangi the Sky Father and Papa the Earth Mother? Then it was seen that the Maruiwi were taking it for granted.

The captives said that it happened every year. The weather grew chilly as the days shortened. There was a season of much wind, heavy rain, and great cold. One had to huddle over a fire for warmth. You left shelter only when hunger drove you to seek food. But there always came a time when the days became long again, and once more you had warmth and sunshine.

Before long bitter winds were sweeping through houses which, like those of the homeland, had been built with open sides. Walls of raupo reeds had to be built and a fire kept burning in the centre of each home. It grew too cold to take the daily bath in the river.

The sweet-potato vines in the garden withered, so the tubers were dug and stored in baskets hung from the rafters, with the best ones reserved for seed. On some days it was an ordeal to go out fishing, hunting, or to dig up fern roots. The days continued to shorten, and the sun was seen seldom. Finally came a spell of weather which showed the people that never previously had they known **real cold.**

It began with a hazy sky and a cutting east wind at dawn. The wind veered to the north, the clouds thickened, and an icy rain began to fall. Then came a period of calm, followed by low, yellowish clouds driving up from the south. Squalls of hail rattled on the thatch. Maui ran outside, gathered some of the pellets of ice, and watched them melt in the warmth of his hand.

There *was* a rock which turned to water, he thought, remembering Rehua's story of the canoe crew which had seen white islands floating on the sea.

"This isn't a nice country!" Ngaio wailed, when he returned. "It's a dreadful place!" She wiped away the tears which ran from her smoke-inflamed eyes and drew the wrapping of tapa cloth closer around her body.

"Those Maruiwi say it'll be warm again in a couple of moons," Hauka said, as he put more wood on the fire and blew it into a blaze.

"I hope we're not all dead before then," Ngaio grumbled.

"You boys can get warm helping to saw some of this pounamu stone," said a man on the other side of the fire.

Dragging one end of a wooden slat, Maui reflected that the cold weather had been as big a surprise to Rehua as to anyone. On his previous visit the old man had seen the country when the days were long and warm. What could be the cause of these short days? Was the tunnel under the earth, through which the sun passed every night, longer here? But that wouldn't explain it. How could a tunnel grow longer and then shorter in one place, yet remain the same length under the island where he had been born?

"Before the next time of cold comes we must lay in a big store of dried eel and fish meat," Hauka suggested, when he and Maui paused in their work to put fresh sand and water into the cut.

"Yes, and bring in a stack of dry firewood," Kura said crossly. She coughed, then added, "This wet wood's smoking the place out!"

It was dreadfully cold that night. They had to huddle close to the fires, wrapped in every mat and piece of tapa they possessed. Morning showed a sky clear except for a few small clouds racing across it, but until noon patches of unmelted hailstone lay piled against rocks and the walls of houses.

Later in the day the sky was cloudless and the wind dropped, but in the shadows your breath steamed as if you were on fire inside. Every one went out fishing with hooks and lines. They were lucky enough to catch sufficient for several meals. Before dusk they hunted for dry wood and brought home stacks of it. That night the cold was worse. When Maui went out next morning he found a strange whiteness extended to the country all around the village.

His feet numb and his teeth chattering, Maui examined the whiteness on the bushes, grass, and stones. It was composed of grains of what looked like salt, yet it turned to water when you scraped it off and picked it up. Suddenly he realized the truth. When water became very cold it turned into a kind of stone, but this melted to water again when warmed.

Later in the morning the whiteness vanished from the open ground, but still lingered in the shadows. Suddenly shouts of dismay sent every one running to the gardens. All the young breadfruit, paper mulberry, banana, plantain, and taro plants looked as if they had been scorched by fire. Presently it was found that the young coconut sprouts on the shore were in the same state. Within a few days all were brown and dead.

The gardeners prayed that the plants would shoot again from the roots, but only the taro and mulberries did so.

"We'll never drink coconut water again, or eat bananas and breadfruit," Kura said sadly.

When the warm days returned and the winter was only an unpleasant memory the two Maruiwi disappeared one night, taking with them some very fine mats and a pounamu adze. A few of the men tried to run them down, but lost their tracks.

"They taught us a lot, but that adze was a high price to pay for it," was Rehua's comment.

Before long there was another nasty surprise. A strange hush fell on the land, with all the birds silent. Before anyone could comment there was a rumbling as if a thunderstorm was underground, then the earth heaved and shook. They were still discussing it when it happened again.

The two Maruiwi had mentioned this thing, but the reality was far more alarming than anyone had expected. Next morning there was a shock so severe that people were thrown off their feet, the whare houses creaked like baskets as they swayed, the water in the river jumped into waves, and the sea, with a dreadful snoring sound, drained away from the land, until rocks never seen previously were exposed. Then it returned in a great wave which rushed far up the beach.

One day a man who had been out searching for wild-duck eggs staggered back to the village. He was so exhausted that at first he could only point to the north-west and gasp, "Taua!" When he had recovered a little he panted out the news that a taua of fighting-men, about fifty strong, was advancing towards them.

"Pararaka is with them!" he added.

The people were incredulous. Pararaka had been sent away from their island in a small canoe! How could he have come here? But the man was positive.

"I saw him! He walks beside the leader of the taua! I sighted them as they came through the bushes, but they didn't see me. I crept away, keeping under cover. They'll be here soon!"

Every one started to talk. Some were for fighting in defence of the village; others said it would be madness to oppose so strong a force. Better get into their canoe and escape while they had time!

"Silence!" Rehua said sternly. "There is one hope." He looked at the narrow neck of land which connected the bluff with the river-bank. "Get the spare anchor rope. Stretch it through the bushes over there, knee-high from the ground. Tie it to stakes which must be driven in firmly. Where it shows hide it with small branches.

"Take your stand a man-length behind it. When the front rank of the charging enemy trips over it strike at their heads, then fight those which follow."

He looked at the women. "Stand behind your men, armed with digging-sticks. Don't strike at the heads of any enemies who break through. Jab them in the stomachs, like this." He demonstrated with a lunge of his walking-staff.

"I shall go out and see if I can reason with them. If they are bent on fighting I'll try to make them angry so they'll charge instead of making a cautious attack."

He beckoned to Maui. "Follow me, keeping hidden. Creep as close as you dare. Hear what is said. When I warn you, come back here to alert the people." He paused to look at his little band of followers.

"It will be my last service to you. May Tu, God of War, favour our cause!"

His head held high, the old chief went off alone to meet the enemy.

9

THE BATTLE OF THE FISHING-NET

Crouching in a patch of bracken fern and peering through the stems, Maui saw Rehua stand upon a low mound to await the arrival of the taua war party. When the band of armed men drew near the boy's skin prickled with superstitious fear, for Pararaka was indeed with them.

"What brings you on my land?" Rehua inquired, when the taua halted a few paces away.

"Your land!" sneered the leader. "We are the Manianga, and we were here long before you! This land is ours, and you have no right on it. As for what we want..." He glanced at the *Tere-Moana*, moored above her own reflection in the calm water.

"As a punishment for settling here without our permission you can hand over that canoe, your pounamu stone, your dogs, and any of your women pretty enough to be worth taking back to our pa as slaves. Then we'll let the rest of you go free to find land somewhere else."

Rehua pretended to be surprised. "Haven't you the skill to make a canoe of your own?" he inquired.

It brought a growl of anger from the war party. "We can build better craft than that clumsy thing!" snarled their leader. "Fine canoes with double hulls, like the one which brought more people from our Hawaiki to join us last year!"

Rehua frowned at Pararaka, as if seeing and recognizing him for the first time. He raised his staff to point. "The gods are angry with that tapu-breaking fool," he said contemptuously. "He'll bring disaster on you."

"The gods favour me!" Pararaka bellowed, shaking his

F

club. "They saw how unjustly you treated me, so they guided me to where some people coming here were able to pick me up with their big canoe!"

So that explained Pararaka's presence, thought Maui. It wasn't so wonderful, after all. He listened to the sound of stakes being driven at the village and prayed that the defence scheme would be successful.

"I don't wonder at you wanting our girls," Rehua remarked, with a curt laugh. "If yours are like you in looks they must be a sorry lot. Did your fathers marry Maruiwi women?"

The audacity of this insult left the taua speechless for a few moments, then they broke into howls of anger. Some advanced towards the old chief, but their leader ordered them back.

Rehua's conduct puzzled him. What could this old man with the grey hair and the tattooed face hope to gain by making them angry? It couldn't be a trick to hold their attention while his followers sneaked up and attacked them from behind, for they stood on open ground, except for a patch of fern on the left—and that wasn't big enough to cover more than a few men.

"You want to steal our pounamu stone?" Rehua mocked. "That does make sense, anyway. You wouldn't have the pluck to sail through the stormy seas to the place where it's found."

This time the leader of the taua had difficulty in restraining the more impetuous of his followers.

"Be warned!" Rehua said, in a stern and ominous tone. "Go home at once!" He still faced the crowd, but Maui knew it was meant for him. He crept back through the ferns, gained the cover of some bushes, and ran to the village. As he looked around for Ruapara he heard a woman say to her husband, "I know what's caused this! Those two dirty Maruiwi creatures you brought home have betrayed us!"

"There are fifty," Maui informed Ruapara. "Pararaka is with them. A big canoe bound for this land came across him far out on the ocean and brought him here."

The last stake was driven and the rope strained taut, with one end tied to a tree and the other hitched round a rock; then it was lashed with cord to the tops of the stakes and camouflaged wherever necessary with bits of bush stuck in the ground.

When the men took up their positions behind it their line looked dreadfully thin, for they had to stand a man-length apart to cover the ground. The women, some of whom were due to have babies soon, formed a second line behind their husbands, with digging-sticks in their hands.

Gripping the beautiful club that had been Hikurangi's parting gift, Maui stood behind Ruapara. He hoped to kill or disable at least one enemy before he himself was struck down. It was sad to die when you were so young. . . . He had planned to do so many things when he grew up. . . . Somebody tugged at his arm, and he turned to see Kura, pale and shaking, yet wearing a determined expression.

"That sham fight back on our Hawaiki!" she panted. "The one when most of your followers had to be declared dead, because the other side had hit them on the head with leaf-stalks. Remember how you won, though you were only four to their nine?"

Hope leaped in Maui's heart. Why hadn't he thought of it himself? Ruapara listened to what he said, at first impatiently, then with keen attention. If only there was still time to do it! His command sent two women running to fetch a large and heavy bundle.

The men worked in frantic haste. They could hear the voice of Rehua in the distance, still gaining precious time for them. The new scheme was completed just as there was a final chorus of angry yells, followed by a single cry of defiance from the old chief and then an ominous silence.

'Pretend to be dismayed when you see how numerous

they are," Ruapara warned, as he hurried along the line for
a final inspection. "Fall back a pace, then another step
after that. Look as if you might break and fly before their
charge reaches us. But when I shout, act together!"

He looked at the line of women. "Cry out to be spared.
Tell them they can have all we own if they leave you
unharmed." He took his place in the line just as the taua
appeared.

Rehua had played his part well, for anger made the
attackers reckless. They formed up hastily, howling threats,
then came bounding over the low bushes. They gave deri-
sive yells when they saw the defenders shuffling back in
what they took for terror, while behind them their women
screamed for mercy.

Men in the front rank of the attackers were already raising clubs to strike when they tripped over the hidden rope
and went sprawling. The rear ranks stumbled into them,
then the fifteen men defending the village stooped, grasped
the sinker line of the great fishing-net which had been
spread on the ground before them, and flung it up and
forward.

Weighted by stones spaced a leg-length apart, the net
fell over the disorganized attackers, entangling them in the
cord meshes. It was soon over. Fifteen men and two boys
struck at the heads under the net, while an equal number
of women and girls thrust like furies with the sharp points
of digging-sticks. Within a few moments there was only a
group of men striking at a sole survivor, who dodged about
as he tried to tear free with hands and teeth.

"Hold!" shouted Ruapara, when he saw who it was. He
came close to stare at Pararaka, bruised, bleeding from a
dozen wounds, but still defiant.

"Breaking a tapu brings its own punishment," the priest
said ominously. "The gods spared you for a time—but only
so your foolish counsel could bring disaster on those who
attacked us."

Pararaka, biting at the cords like a shark worrying a carcass, nearly managed to break free from the meshes, but a man flung another fold of net over him.

"Now comes your fate!" Ruapara added, bracing his feet and measuring the distance with his eye. "May those poor fools you misled give you no peace in the next world!"

Kura turned her head away with a shudder, and put her hands over her ears to shut out the sound of the blow from the club. Then the people turned to look at one another as they began to realize what they had done. Fifteen men and two boys, backed by seventeen women and girls, had defeated fifty men—had killed every one of them, without suffering a scratch!

It was incredible, yet there on the ground, tangled in the deadly meshes of the great fishing-net, were the huddled bodies of the dead. Seventeen men against fifty! What a tale to tell to your children in years to come! A woman began to sob with relief.

"Great is our mana!" cried a man, shaking his club at the dead foes. "Well are they known as the Manianga," said another, rolling a body on to its back with his foot.

"See how they show their teeth in a cruel snarl, even in death."

It was Maui who brought them back to earth. "What about Rehua?" he said. The rejoicing ceased abruptly, and four men hurried away. The long, keen wails of tangi mourning broke from the women as Rehua's body was carried home and laid on his sleeping-mats.

"Never was there a more noble chief," Ruapara said brokenly. "Truly did he carry out the duty of a warrior to die in defence of his land!"

With the cries of the women ringing in their ears, the men disposed of the bodies of their dead enemies. Next day, solemnly and reverently, they buried Rehua on the little mound where he had stood to defy the enemy.

"This spot will be tapu ground as long as we can keep fires burning on our land," said Ruapara.

Some men went out hunting that afternoon. They soon returned, each carrying a large bundle on his shoulder. "We discovered the Manianga camp," said the first to arrive. "See what we found there." He spread out six cloaks for inspection.

"The twine is made from the thread in the leaves of that flax plant which grows in the swamps," said one of the women as she examined the prizes.

"See how moa or kiwi feathers are tied into each knot of the weave!" cried another.

A third woman draped a cloak over her shoulders. "Such fine garments should do more than keep you warm in cold weather," she commented "Hanging down as they do, the feathers should shed rain like the thatch on a roof."

"And they'll be good to sleep under on a winter night," said a man who had brought one of the bundles. "It looks as if it was kind of those Manianga fools to attack us."

"Now we know how it's done, we can make cloaks like these for ourselves," said Kura. "From now on we must save all the feathers to use in them."

"Make them?" scoffed the man. "Why go to that trouble when we now have one for every person in our tribe, and a whole lot to spare?" He paused to count the prizes. "Every man will have two—one to wear at home and another to put on when he goes out hunting in cold weather!"

Ten days later a party of moa-hunters sighted two men who were following the tracks left by the Manianga taua. They stalked and surrounded the strangers.

"We seek some of our people who came this way," stammered one of the two Manianga as he scanned the grim faces around him.

"Seek them in the next world, then," jeered the leader of the hunters. "You'll find them hard to recognize, though. After we'd killed them all we scattered their bones."

Gasps of horror came from the strangers. To be killed was bad enough, but to exist as bits and pieces in the here-after was a dreadful fate. But how had their taua of fifty warriors met with disaster? That Maruiwi had told them there were only fifteen fighting-men among these new-comers—and Pararaka had said it would be correct.

"So great is our mana that your men could not prevail against us, even at odds of more than three to one," said the leader of the hunters, surmising what the captives were thinking. "Go back and tell your people to send a hundred men next time—but give them better cloaks than the last lot." He glanced contemptuously at the one that he wore. "Our women were disgusted with the poor work in them. As you see, we regard them as fit to wear only when we go out hunting."

Dazed and humiliated, the two men carried the dreadful news back to their tribe.

Ruapara, the new chief, nodded approvingly when he heard the story. "You did well to let those two go free. They'll tell their people it's hopeless to attack us. When the story spreads nobody else will dare to come against us."

There was an unexpected sequel. One morning four medium-sized canoes, crammed with men, women, and children, paddled into the bay. They stopped a hundred paces out from the shore, and their leader called, "We seek a home with you."

"Whence do you come?" Ruapara inquired.

"From the Manianga, the tribe whose fighting-men you slew." This brought a growl of anger from the people on the beach, but it died away when the newcomer explained: "They also attacked my people, the Katahi, without cause, slaying all except me and those you see here. They took us back to their village and made us work as slaves.

"But when we heard how you'd killed all their warriors we seized weapons, took some of their canoes, and set off to see if you would let us live with you."

"Haere mai—you are welcome!" said Ruapara.

Hiki, the leader of the newcomers, had a great deal of information to impart to the men in the council house. That Maruiwi man had betrayed them. The Manianga had listened to his tale of a people few in numbers who possessed many dogs and much pounamu stone like that in the blade of the adze which he carried. Pararaka told them that he had a grudge against these same people and urged the Manianga to attack at once.

"They agreed to do it," Hiki added; "then they killed that Maruiwi man, saying that those who betrayed one lot of people would do the same with others." He gazed with respect at the men around him. "But how did you defeat the big taua they sent against you?"

"Tu has given us great mana as fighters," Rupara replied. He inquired how the relatives of the dead men had taken the news of the crushing defeat.

"Never were there such lamentations," Hiki told him. "There may be trouble in store for you one day, though. The women of the Manianga say they will make their sons exact a terrible utu vengeance when they grow up."

"Utu?" Ruapara echoed. "Why, the blame lies with them! We had done them no wrong, yet they attacked us."

"It's because of the insulting message you sent back about those cloaks. The Manianga women had each spent a year in making one. You said they were fit only to wear out hunting."

Ruapara laughed it off. By the time those Manianga boys grew to manhood his tribe would also have a strong fighting force to oppose them. This new arrival had brought eight boys with him, too. The Manianga could utter threats if it gave them any comfort—but they wouldn't make him lose any sleep!

"What is the name of your tribe—and mine too, seeing we have now joined you?" Hiki inquired.

"We call ourselves the Tere-Moana, after the canoe which brought us here," the chief replied.

"You could make this place easy to defend," Hiki said, looking out at the narrow neck of land on which the battle of the fish-net had been fought. "Put a palisade of stout posts across there, with a ditch before it. Along the inside build a raised bank of earth, on which your men can stand to strike down at attackers. Many villages in this land now have such defence works."

"It is a fine idea," Ruapara said warmly. "When you have rested we must hear more of it."

After the newcomers, who were weary from having paddled all night, had gone to the sleeping-places assigned to them Maui went to where Kura sat at a weaving-frame, copying one of the Manianga cloaks, and told her the news.

"Why do people fight?" she said. "If a tribe hasn't a real grievance they soon think up one. Fancy those Manianga saying we had no right to own pounamu adzes when they had none!"

"Some people are too lazy or clumsy to make fine things

for themselves," Maui suggested. "But when they see others with them they get envious."

He laughed. "Rehua did give them a nasty dig when he said they were afraid to make the voyage down to the place where pounamu stone is found. I think it hurt because there happened to be a lot of truth in it."

"Yes, and some people seem able to justify everything they do," Kura said thoughtfully. "Even killing others. But it makes me sick inside to even think of it."

"You jabbed at those men under the net as hard as any-one," he reminded her.

"That's different. I was helping to protect my home— like a mother bird defending her nest. But don't remind me of that battle. I want to forget it."

10

MAUI GROWS UP

When Maui grew to manhood he was able to gratify his ambition to explore. As a boy he had often climbed the mountain on his island home, when the weather was clear, to gaze on the surrounding seascape and at the far-off hills of Oamu. Always he had wondered what lay beyond the horizon's rim.

Since his landing in this new country the distant hills had seemed to entice him to see what lay beyond them; the mountains even farther off had challenged him to climb them and stand upon their summits, gazing at the world below. Now he set off to do those things.

Accompanied by Hauka and Wera, the son of Hiki, he would go off for days or even weeks, visiting inland country where the feet of men had never trodden before. One of their first discoveries was a forest of big trees, growing on the upper reaches of the river which ran past the pa village of their people. Some were even larger than the forest giant from which the hull of the *Tere-Moana* canoe had been hewn.

There was no lack of food. Fern root could be dug almost anywhere, eels were plentiful in creek pools, and the wild pigeons were so tame that you could knock them out of a tree with a long stick.

Wandering on, they came to an area which at first they feared to enter. In places the ground steamed as does an umu oven pit when it is opened, strange smells hung in the air, and in some pools the water was too hot for you to keep a toe in it for a moment. They agreed that no legend told of stranger things.

Another journey took them far to the south-west. Kept awake by the cold one night when they camped on the crest of a ridge where there was no firewood, they felt the ground shake repeatedly and saw a glow appear in the south. It broadened, until it illuminated a towering pillar of smoke, then bright red objects rose slowly in the air, curved over and sank to earth again, accompanied by sounds like far-off thunder.

When dawn came they saw a distant mountain shooting out fire, red-hot boulders, steam, and smoke.

"One of Rehua's legends told of a time when the people lived in a land where the hills rumbled and spat flames!" Maui cried. "Now we see it for ourselves!"

"I wonder if people first obtained fire from one of these burning mountains," said Wera.

"What stay-at-home people miss!" Hauka remarked. "When we return from a trip others are eager to hear us talk of what we've seen, yet they won't accompany us to look on such things themselves."

On one trip, after making a wide detour to avoid trespassing on the Manianga tribe's land, they headed north into a pleasant country of valleys and streams which ran to the distant sea-coast. From a hill-top they sighted a small village surrounded by a palisade of stakes. For some time they debated the wisdom of approaching it, but Wera persuaded his companions to take the risk.

They halted a hundred paces from the pa and asked for admittance. The people who lived there were very suspicious at first. They asked many questions while they scanned the surrounding country for signs of a hostile force. Their attitude changed when they learned that the visitors came from the tribe which had scored such a notable victory over the savage, untrustworthy Manianga.

They knew that tribe only too well, they declared, as they entertained their guests on the open marae ground among the houses. They themselves were the Motu tribe, whose ancestors had arrived in Aotearoa four generations previously.

At first they had lived on the coast, but the attacks of the Manianga had driven them to this inland country. The

visitors stayed with them for the duration of a moon and learned several new methods for securing food.

One was to build a little hut under a tree whose berries were ripe. You hid inside it, armed with a light and very long spear. When a fat wild pigeon alighted to eat the fruit you moved the spear gently into position, gave a swift thrust, and impaled the bird on the bone barb.

Every year shoals of the tiny, delicious inanga fish came up the creeks from the sea. They were caught in very fine nets made from flax threads. When the raupo reeds were in flower the pollen from them could be collected, moistened, moulded into cakes, and baked.

The men of the Motu were envious when they heard of the pounamu stone. They had nothing half so good for the blades of tools. This made Maui thoughtful. It would be very handy to have these people for friends. On the night before his party left he issued an invitation.

"Let two of your young men come with us. We will make them a gift of pounamu to take home with them."

The chief was delighted with the offer and selected Hotua and Rewi to make the trip.

As soon as he was back in his own pa Maui made a report to Ruapara, then went in search of Kura. He found her at a weaving-frame—but this time she wasn't delighted to see him. "How long before you go wandering off again?" she said coldly.

"What's wrong?" he said, surprised at this reception.

"Wrong?" she said indignantly. "I'm tired of the way you treat me. You never mention marriage now. All you care about is wandering off, leaving me here to worry about your safety. I'll look for another man to marry."

Maui was dismayed. He didn't want anyone else for a wife. Kura wasn't beautiful. During the last few years her features had become heavy, with thick eyebrows. Her body had filled out until her arms and legs were muscled like those of a man—yet he loved her. No other girls attracted him—even the very pretty ones whom he had seen at the Motu pa.

He had been thoughtless where she was concerned! For a few moments he thought of begging her to forgive him, then he remembered what he had heard the older men say. Never argue with a woman, for she would always out-talk you. Nor should you be humble with her. The best thing to do was to make a plain statement of fact and leave her to think it over.

"All right," he said curtly. "My wandering, as you call it, has a purpose. We must have allies, in case the Manianga persuade other tribes to join in an attack on us. On this last trip I made a valuable friendship with the Motu people."

Kura kept her head averted, but she was no longer sure of herself.

"You may as well have the gifts I brought," he went on. "On the way home we camped in the hills out there. Something rustled in the leaves near my head. I struck at it and found it was small and furry. I hung it in a bush. When the daylight came I recognized it as a kiore rat."

"A kiore?" she cried. "Then we were wrong in thinking those we brought from our Hawaiki had died out!"

"They must have gone to the hills, knowing there was more food there. We found their little paths everywhere, so we made traps and caught some." He opened his basket and produced a cage containing eleven fat rats. "I brought them for you." From the basket he took a leaf-wrapped package and opened it to disclose two plump pigeons.

The basket held a third parcel. He undid some matting and took out an oval wooden box, beautifully carved. When he lifted the lid Kura saw that it held some pretty black and white huia feathers. "For your hair," he explained. "The Motu girls wear such feathers in a band around the head."

"These fine gifts show you realize how you've neglected me," she commented, but there was no anger in her tone now. Maui stood up.

"I must go to a meeting in the council house," he told her and walked out.

That evening Kura came to him and stood with her gaze on the ground. Her voice was low. "Those rats were delicious. I shared them with Ngaio. She helped me eat the pigeons too. That's a lovely little box." She moved closer to him. "I didn't mean what I said about marrying somebody else."

"Don't ever talk like that again, then," he said sternly, then set her heart fluttering by adding, "In the morning I'll speak to Ruapara about our wedding."

Kura was glad to find Maui masterful. No woman could respect a spineless man. Her thoughts went to the wedding. She must hurry to finish that new feather cloak so it would be ready in time. . . .

Next day, when Maui took the visitors down to show them the *Tere-Moana* canoe he found water ankle-deep in it. "The bailing out has been neglected!" he growled, taking one of the wooden scoops. His two companions helped to throw out the water. Presently one cried, "It is entering through a hole here!"

Maui moved to investigate. When he put his hand down he felt spongy wood, and a prod from his finger made the hole larger. His shouts brought helpers, and the canoe was hauled upon the bank, where they soon found that the hull was rotten below the waterline.

Here was the end of their dreams of sailing back in her to their Hawaiki, taking a gift of pounamu stone and returning with more of their people, with a few pigs as well!

"I can't make it out," said Ruapara. "Back on our island a canoe made from tamanu wood lasts for half a lifetime."

"Not if kept in fresh water," Rewi pointed out. "This one would still be sound if you'd put it on the bank where it is now, with a roof to protect it from the weather."

I should have known that, Ruapara thought sadly. But, of course, there were so many tasks to occupy your hands and mind here. The days weren't long enough for all you had to do. . . . Hunting, fishing, working in the gardens, keeping the houses in repair. . . . Erecting that palisade and digging the trench to fortify the bluff had taken a long time. . . .

The women had no leisure, either. Babies were arriving in an endless succession. Clothes had to be made to protect the little ones from the winter cold. . . .

"Never mind," said Maui. "When the children grow up we'll make another canoe like it from one of the great trees I saw farther up the river. We can float the hull down here."

The sight of the great canoe weathering on the bank was a constant reproach to the Tere-Moana people. They recalled how gallantly she had ridden out the big storm. They thought of all the work which had gone into her building. Finally they decided her fate.

The beautifully carved figurehead and stern-piece were removed and stored in one of the houses, to be used for the next big canoe they built. The outrigger was dismantled and placed within the hull, together with the mast, what was left of the sail, and the remains of the fishing-net which had helped to defeat the Manianga warriors, but which had never since been used, being tapu because the blood of men had been shed on it.

Alongside her they dug a big trench, the full length of the canoe and a man-height wide. Into this they lowered the hull, as if burying a chief. After the earth had been piled over her large stones were set up at each end to show what her length had been. On top of one of the marker stones they placed her rock anchor for coming generations to see and revere.

Around the area they placed a fence of totara posts and rails, to protect ground which would be tapu in future. Ruapara said that the same amount of work put towards the upkeep of the canoe would have meant having a craft that was still seaworthy.

"But it's too late to think of it now," he added.

Later a team of men went up to the forest that Maui had discovered, felled some medium-sized trees, turned them into fishing-canoes capable of carrying ten people at a time, and floated them down to the village. They also selected a huge tree standing on the river-bank and put a tapu sign on it, to show it was reserved for the ocean-going canoe which would make a trip back to their Hawaiki some day.

One morning Rewi watched the Tere-Moana children at play. Boys skipped flat stones on the river, spun tops, or

G

built a miniature pa of reed-stalks. Some girls wove flower garlands, while others used them to decorate a playhouse.

After a time Rewi went away, and returned carrying some straight, thin manuka sticks. One was the length of his arm, and the rest three times as long. He tied a piece of cord to the end of the short stick, turning it into a whip; then he stuck the thin end of a long stick into the ground at an angle. He smiled at the boys who had gathered to watch.

"This is how my people fling spears to a great distance," he explained, as he wound a few turns of the free end of the cord around the long stick near its thick end. When he gave the whip a powerful jerk the long stick sailed like a dart through the air, to bury its point in the ground a long way off.

The boys rushed away to cut similar sticks, and soon they were all playing with kotaha whip-flung spears, which they directed at their reed-stalk pa, pretending that an enemy held it.

Then Tuatane, one of the boys who had come with Hiki's party of refugees had a new idea. He ran off, and returned with a burning stick. "I'll chase those Manianga out of there!" he shouted, as he flung it at the reed palisade.

The flight through the air fanned the glowing end to flame, and within a few moments the sides of the play pa were flaring and crackling.

"What foolery is this?" Maui said angrily, after he and some other men had beaten out the flames with boughs. "Do you want to burn the village?" But after the shamefaced Tuatane had explained what he had done Maui became very thoughtful.

Later, in a spot free from observation, he made experiments by throwing fire-sticks at a small patch of dead bracken. He found he could set it alight from a distance of nearly forty paces.

He sought out Hiki and took him away for a consultation. "You were a captive in the Manianga pa, so you know its lay-out. Draw a plan of it here on the sand," he directed. When it was finished Maui studied the sketch and inquired the various distances between houses and from the buildings to the palisades.

When Hotua and Rewi set out for home, each carrying a lump of pounamu stone on his shoulder, Maui walked some distance with them. At parting he said, "This is for the ear of your chief alone. If ever we have to join forces against the Manianga we should be able to take their pa without trouble."

11

WIFE OF MAUI

When their wedding-day arrived Maui and Kura sat on a special mat. Ruapara chanted the Ohaoha prayer over them, in which he sought the blessing of the gods on their union. Like the canoe-hauling song, it was very ancient. It included words and phrases whose meaning nobody knew now.

Then Utea, the assistant priest, recited the list of Maui's ancestors, beginning with his father and going back to the days when the gods walked the earth. After this each family group came up to lay their gifts on the mat. When every one had told Kura how fine she looked in her new cloak, with the huia feathers in her headband, and had praised the manly bearing of Maui, the heads of the households made their speeches.

Maui's duty, they said, was to protect his wife, to provide her with food and the materials to make clothing, and to keep the roof over her head watertight.

To Kura they said, "Cook his food in the way he likes best. Have a new cloak ready for him when the old one wears out. Greet him with a smile when he comes home tired from hunting, fishing, or working in the garden."

To every speaker the young couple replied, "We shall be true to each other until death claims us."

When Ruapara made the principal speech he referred to the change in the living habits of the people rendered necessary by the conditions in this new land. On their island birthplace far away to the north-east boys had done the cooking. Here this task had fallen to the women, for men and boys were kept busy with outdoor work. Women had little leisure here, for they also had to make warm clothing as a protection from the cold.

Because conditions here were so much harder than in their Hawaiki there was little time for play. There was also the need to be ever on the alert, in case an enemy made a surprise attack, but they had a noble precept to guide them. Rehua had shown them how a man should live. In him they had known a true Rangatira aristocrat; one of those high-born men who was a father to his people.

He had also shown them how a man should die. By parleying with the enemy he had gained time for his people to make ready their defences. Without him the Manianga could not have been defeated in the battle of the fishing-net. Ruapara paused to survey the rows of attentive faces on the marae.

"Here, with the blessing of the gods, the Tere-Moana will be a great tribe. Tane made us a gift of this new land as a sign of his favour, but we must be worthy of it or it will be taken away."

The ceremony concluded with a great feast. The choicest dishes were offered to the young couple. Some men had spent days out in the hills, trapping kiore rats. Others had speared many wild pigeons. There were also piles of eels and fish, mounds of taro and sweet potatoes. Finally the open marae ground was sprinkled with water to keep down the dust, and the dancing began.

At dusk Maui and Kura retired to the new house which had been built for them.

A year later a little 'nest-house' was built on the edge of the bluff. Here Kura went to live, accompanied by the two older women who were to help with the birth of her baby. Nobody else came near her, as she was now tapu.

A charcoal fire was kept burning in the hut, for the weather had turned cold. Twice a day food was cooked and taken to a spot near the nest-house by friends, who then retired. When they were out of sight the two tapuhi maternity nurses came out to get it. On the morning of the fifth day a wailing from the little hut showed that the baby had been born. Soon every one knew it was a boy. But Maui didn't get as much as a glimpse of his son for another eight days.

Then came the morning of the tohi baptism. A little procession left the pa, headed by the assistant priest. Kura followed, the baby in her arms. Maui walked behind her, then the two nurses. Ruapara walked at the rear.

They crossed the undulating plan to a spot where a clear creek joined the river. Here some mats were spread on the ground. Ruapara took off his cloak and stepped into the water, naked except for a small apron. In his hand he held a little green branch.

"Io, the parentless," he whispered solemnly, "Io, the great parent, I am a tapu person, learned in the mysteries, so I am fit to conduct this ceremony." He dipped the branch in the water, and Kura, standing on the mats, handed him the baby.

Facing the east, where the sunrise provided a daily symbol of birth and life, and now speaking loudly, Ruapara said as he sprinkled water from the branch on the head of the baby, "Your name is Perere. May you become a great man, skilled in the arts, brave in war."

He pinched the baby's nostrils with his finger and thumb, pressed the palm of his hand over its mouth, and ducked it under the water, at the same time immersing his own body. Then the wet and wailing infant was returned to the mother.

Now the assistant priest handed Ruapara a stick cage holding a little bird which had been netted on the previous night. The shivering chief came out of the water, took the bird in his hand, touched the head of the baby with it, and let it fly away.

"Go, tell the gods that their mana has entered this

child," he said. A hole was dug on the bank of the near-by river, and five pebbles were placed in it, to indicate that the child had been born in the fifth moon of the year. As the earth was replaced Ruapara said, "This is the baptismal place of the boy Perere. Those stones indicate his ownership in a share of the tribal land in which they are buried."

When the party returned to the pa every one was on the marae ground to welcome the baby, now officially a member of the tribe. After several men had made speeches a feast was served.

As soon as they were alone in their house Maui gazed at his first-born, while Kura suckled it. She smiled fondly as she looked at the little head, on which the hair showed already as a thick, dark down.

"This is the proudest moment of my life!" said Maui. "Greater even than when I was chosen to be one of the canoe crew or when my idea of using a hidden fishing-net gave us victory over the Manianga!"

Kura was happy to find him so pleased with the son she had borne him, but inwardly she was amused at the idea of comparing pride in a child with anything else on earth.

Men had the advantage in most things, but the joy of motherhood was something they could never know. . . .

She sang softly to the little one as she rocked him in her arms.

During the following seven years she gave birth to four more children, the next three being girls. When the younger son was five years old and could be cared for by friends she spoke to her husband about the thing which was always in the back of her mind: the building of another great ocean-going canoe and a visit to their Hawaiki.

"How much longer must we wait?" she pleaded. "We now have plenty of strong young men to do the work. Is that big tree up in the hills to stand there till it dies of old age?"

"The young men can't see why we're so anxious to visit our homeland," he replied. "They are unwilling to tackle such a big task."

Kura knew this, but couldn't understand it. Over and over again she had told groups of young people about her Hawaiki, where the weather was never cold, you could swim in the sea every day of the year, and trees bore sweet fruits.

They listened with interest, but the homesickness of the older people was something beyond their grasp. To them this new land was home. Used to the cold from birth, they felt the winters far less than those born on the warm island far away. A description of baked pork left them unmoved. What could be nicer than moa eggs, eel-meat, or fish? They had no craving for things which they had never tasted, such as coconuts, breadfruit, or bananas. Kura sighed as she thought of their outlook. They didn't worry if she never saw her family, friends, or homeland again.

One warm summer day, when she was giving her youngest child a swimming lesson, Kura saw a fishing-canoe return to the bay. The men in it were paddling furiously, yet their shouts conveyed no note of alarm. They were still too far off for her to make out what they were saying. . . .

Then she gasped, for the cause of their excitement was revealed. Around the northern headland came a twin-hulled canoe, its triangular sail bellying in the wind. On the deck platform which connected the two hulls were some thirty men, women, and children, all waving pieces of white tapa.

By the time Kura had dried her big body and had put on her cloak an excited throng had gathered on the beach. Eager questions were shouted to the fishermen. Had these people come from their Hawaiki? Who was on board?

The fishermen were now too out of breath to shout. They did not speak until they had beached their canoe; then they panted out what they had learned. Those people were strangers. They had come from the great island of Tahiti-Nui. They sought a place where they could rest before voyaging on in search of vacant country.

The sail of the twin-hulled canoe was lowered a hundred paces out from the beach, and the man in command shouted, "We come in peace, seeking your hospitality. May we land?"

"Haere mai!" Ruapara welcomed them, and sent fishing-canoes out to bring them ashore as soon as they had dropped their anchor stone.

Before long the men from Tahiti were being entertained at a hastily prepared feast, while the Tere-Moana women fed the wives and children of the newcomers in a separate group. When they had eaten their leader told his story.

"My father was a high chief on Tahiti-Nui. After he died I told my brother we should share the land and people between us, seeing that our elder brother, the ariki first-born, was dead. He wouldn't agree.

" 'I'm older than you,' " he said. " 'The leadership is mine by right.' " We became angry with each other, then we fought. He beat me. When the people saw me lying senseless on the ground most of them went over to my brother's side. Only those you see with me now remained faithful.

" 'I will be merciful because the same mother bore us,' " said my brother. " 'Take one of the canoes. Sail away with any who are foolish enough to accompany you. Find land of your own. Be gone by noon.' " So we put our weapons and clothes, with such food and water as we could gather in so short a time, aboard the canoes and sailed.

"I knew of no country where we might find a new home except the one found by Kupe. As we had insufficient food for so long a voyage we went first to Rarotonga, but for a time the people wouldn't let us land. 'You can have some coconuts,' they told us, 'then you must sail away at once.' But they relented when we begged them to show pity because of the young children aboard.

"We soon saw why they hadn't wanted us to land. Their crops had failed because little rain had fallen for a long time. They had nothing to eat themselves except fish and coconuts. We rested with them for a few days, then sailed, taking all the nuts they could spare. It took eighteen days for us to reach this land of Aotearoa. We made our landfall in the bay north of this one, but I didn't like the look of the people there."

"They are the treacherous, spiteful Manianga," said Ruapara.

"So we sailed down the coast till we sighted your fishermen," the Tahitian added. "They invited us to visit your pa. Where can we find unclaimed land?"

"Down there," Ruapara replied, pointing to the south. "Our country runs to the top of the range which extends to the coast. Nobody claims the land beyond it."

While the weary voyagers slept their hosts held a conference. All agreed that the newcomers seemed to be good people. Maui began to frown thoughtfully. Finally he said, "An idea has come to me. The most precious thing in this land is pounamu stone."

"The Manianga covet our store of it," Ruapara agreed.

"Then let us borrow the fine canoe belonging to our guests, sail down to the south land, and bring back another cargo of it," Maui went on. "Some, of course, must go to the Tahitians. Some we will add to our own hoard. The rest we can distribute, giving a large share to our friends the Motu tribe. The Manianga get none, of course." He saw that every one was listening attentively.

"Then all the other tribes won't want to attack us to get pounamu, seeing they have enough for their needs. They will be on our side if the Manianga come against us."

A roar of approval greeted Maui's remarks. When the leader of the Tahitians awakened they showed him an adze with a blade of the precious green stone and put the proposition to him. He tried the tool on a log of wood.

"I have heard of this stone," he said, "but never did I think it could be so good. Yes, you can have our canoe—and I'll go with you. I'd like to see where this stone is found—and I can look at the land as we sail down the coast and pick out a site for our new home."

When the women who had come in the canoe had finished their meal one of them apologized for the quantity of eel-meat and fern root she had eaten. "I just couldn't resist these good things after living on nothing but coconuts for so many days," she explained.

Kura gave a cry of surprise. Coconuts! Had they any left? She was told there were scores. "Will you let me have a few?" she said breathlessly. They told her to help herself.

Snatching up a basket, she ran down to the beach, flung off her cloak, and swam out to the canoe. There they were —a great pile of them. Her mouth watering, she put a dozen of the big, hairy, husked nuts into the basket and swam ashore, floating her treasure ahead of her.

"One of the wonderful foods of my Hawaiki," she said to her assembled family. She bored out the eyes of several nuts and distributed them, then sucked the milk from one herself. When they were handed back she sawed around the lines on them with a sharp flake of stone and split them open. "Now you scrape out this sweet white meat," she directed. "When they're clean you can use them for nice little bowls."

"Now I know why you want to go back to your Hawaiki," Perere said. "This food has a wonderful taste."

Kura's eyes filled with tears. The flavour of the coconut meat and the well-known odour made her heart ache with longing to see her homeland again. Abruptly she ran out of the house, stood on the edge of the bluff, and stared at the Tahitians' canoe. Now there could be no talk about the immense amount of work entailed in building a craft to make the voyage! Here was one, ready to be used!

She waited impatiently for the conference to end. When Maui appeared at last she panted out her great idea. He listened with a smile of agreement.

"Think of it!" she said happily. "We'll drink coconut water again, we'll eat bananas, we'll see our families and friends! Then we'll come back, bringing more of our people and pigs, fowls, and another lot of plants!"

"That canoe must go first to the great south land for more pounamu," he told her, "but when it returns we can borrow it for a trip home——" He broke off to listen to a shout from the sentry on duty at the defence palisade.

"What's this? A messenger approaching?" He hurried away, and was gone for a long time. When he returned, his face wore a grim expression. "There won't be a trip home," he said curtly. "That messenger was sent by our friends the Motu."

Kura gave a wail of disappointment. She could guess what Maui was going to say.

"The Manianga plan to avenge the deaths of their warriors this summer," he went on. "An escaped slave took the news to the Motu. Help me prepare for a journey. Ruapara is sending me to spy on the enemy."

12

THE VENGEANCE OF THE MANIANGA

Kura's hands shook with anger as she prepared food for her husband to take on his dangerous mission. A wonderful opportunity to visit her far-off Hawaiki must be lost—and those vindictive old Manianga women were to blame! What right had they to bring up their sons to exact an utu vengeance from the Tere-Moana tribe? Hadn't their dead husbands started it by that unprovoked attack?

"It's no use talking of rights and wrongs," Maui told her, after she had voiced her bitter thoughts. "We have to face the facts. In the Manianga pa, two days' journey away, are more than a hundred young fighting-men, eager to avenge the deaths of their fathers. If we let them make another surprise attack the advantage will be on their side. This time we'll strike first."

"You'll risk sending some men away in that Tahitian canoe to get more pounamu?" she inquired.

"Only ten are needed for a crew," he pointed out. "It won't be much of a risk. According to that messenger, they can't be ready to attack us for several moons."

Maui refused to divulge his plans. He set off, accompanied by his trusted friend Hauka and a couple of young men whom they were training as scouts. Avoiding all tracks after they left the Tere-Moana tribal lands, they made their way through the hills until they reached a ridge from which they could look down on the Manianga pa. Here they kept hidden, lighting no fires and living on the cooked and dried food which they carried.

In the distance they could see the young men of their

foes training. The taua which carried out exercises in attacking was about a hundred and twenty strong. "Lucky we had that warning," Hauka commented. "They are a formidable force. Look how they keep together when they carry out a practice charge!"

"We have time to prepare for the coming war, though," Maui remarked. "They can't attack us till the kumara crops are harvested in the autumn." He moved apart from his companions in order to be free to think. Gradually he worked out a plan of campaign.

"Let us now confer with our friends the Motu," he said at length.

They were given a hearty welcome at the Motu pa. After the feast Maui disclosed his plans. "We are allies," he began. "The Manianga are the common enemy. They now have a powerful taua of fighting-men—and I think they intend to attack you first."

The Motu men heard it with dismay, for it confirmed their fears.

"You have only thirty fighting-men to defend this little pa of yours," Maui continued. "Too few for you to sally out to attack an encircling enemy. But if they came here the Manianga would not need to attack you. They could settle down to starve you out."

Gloomy nods confirmed this summary of the position. Maui pointed to a mountain whose summit was visible beyond the head of a near-by valley.

"That high hill looks down on your pa. We can see it from our village. There will be no clouds to hide it in the autumn. Send some of your men off to build a pile of firewood on the summit. Thatch it to keep it dry. Let some of your young men camp at the end of that valley, keeping a watch night and day on your pa.

"If you are attacked those men must hurry to the top of the mountain and light the signal fire. We'll see it and come to your aid. We'll also have men living in the hills

to the west of our country, keeping a watch on our pa.
If we're attacked first they'll send a messenger to tell
you."

"Then we hurry to your aid and take your attackers in
the rear?" the Motu chief suggested. "As you'll do to help
us if we're beseiged?"

"That comes later—if necessary," Maui replied. "Here's
the main point. The one not under attack must go first to
the Manianga pa and destroy it!"

It was greeted with a shout of approval, but then Maui's
old friend Rewi thought he saw a flaw in it. "Your tribe
musters ninety fighting-men," he pointed out. "It is a force
strong enough to storm the Manianga pa when only old
men and the women are left to defend it. But what could
our thirty warriors do? You've seen how formidable are the
Manianga defences!"

"It is a strong position," Maui agreed, "but it has one
terrible weakness. The houses in it are crowded together,
and some are close to the palisade. Have you forgotten the
fire-sticks, Rewi?"

There was a roar of delight when the Motu men grasped
the idea.

"We mustn't fail each other," Maui warned, when his
little party was saying farewell. "If we do the Manianga
may destroy one of us first, then the other."

When the four envoys returned they helped to streng-
then the defences of the Tere-Moana pa. Shortly after this
task was completed the Tahitian canoe came back with a
cargo of pounamu.

Every one then set to work to harvest the crop of kumara
sweet potatoes. The storehouses, elevated on posts, were
swept out and repaired. New carrying baskets were made.
Then the men dug up the tubers, while the women sorted
them and carried them home. When the task was completed Ruapara and Maui called the Tahitians to a conference.

"It's too late in the season for you to settle on country of your own," Ruapara told them. "You wouldn't have time to build houses before the cold, stormy weather arrives. You have no food stored for the winter. Stay with us. You can go off to build a pa of your own when the warm weather comes again."

He was pleased when they accepted the offer. Their six men would be a valuable addition to his forces.

"I still pray that the Manianga won't attack after all," Kura said hopefully, as she lay beside Maui in their house that night.

"War will come as surely as to-morrow's sunrise," he replied. Towards morning they were awakened by shouts from the sentries, and the news was carried from house to house. The people ran out to see a glow on the distant mountain summit.

Before dawn Maui marched off at the head of a taua of ninety-four men. On the following night his force crept close to the Manianga pa in the darkness, and Maui went ahead to reconnoitre the defences. It was indeed a formidable stronghold, he decided.

It stood on the summit of a rise. Every scrap of cover had been removed from the surrounding slopes. On the farther side of a deep ditch was the palisade of stout poles, half as high again as a man and with every stake having a sharp point on top. Behind it was a platform from which the defenders could thrust down with lances at attackers—and behind it was another ditch and a second defence work.

But close to the inside of that second line of stakes he could see, silhouetted against the star-strewn sky, the thatched roofs of the houses. The wind was blowing from the north, and it was strong and dry. Maui crept back to Hauka, his second-in-command.

"We should take it without losing a man," he whispered. "Go off to make a diversion on the other side—but keep back from the fence. Make it look as if we're going to wait for dawn before we attack."

He watched half his force file off into the darkness, then went to the far side of a belt of scrub, where a few men had started a fire with the aid of a stick and a slab of soft wood. He watched the torch-sticks being prepared, and smiled grimly when he heard the shouts of alarm in the pa.

The Manianga were shocked to find their stronghold under attack while most of their fighting-men were away attending to the preliminary task of wiping out the little Motu tribe, but they soon had their defences manned. They shouted words of defiance which changed to jeers when the enemy charged up the slope, halted as if surprised at the strength of the palisade, then withdrew a short distance.

But on the north side the defenders then saw a line of dark figures come up the slope, each carrying several pieces of wood with glowing ends. These attackers halted a few paces from the ditch and began to hurl their torches. Most dropped short of the houses on bare ground, where they were soon extinguished by the women, but a few lodged on a thatched roof.

One was extinguished by a man who climbed the carved barge-board and emptied a gourd of water over it, but from two others flames arose and spread with devastating speed. More torches and flying sparks set fire to other roofs.

Brighter grew the glare and thicker the rolling clouds of smoke; louder the roar and crackle of the flames. The defenders soon realized that they had but two alternatives. They could stay inside to be roasted by the heat as the close-packed houses burned, or they could open the gate and rush out in a body, hoping to break through the encircling attackers and gain the sanctuary of the forest. They chose to break out.

A day's journey away the defenders of the tiny Motu pa had fought off yet another attack, but it was obvious that

H

they could not hold out much longer. Logs used by parties of men as battering-rams had weakened the stake fences in two places. Once the enemy broke through it there would be nothing you could do except try to kill a Manianga or two before you were struck down.

Suddenly one of their sentries gave a shout of joy. "Look over there! Our Tere-Moana allies are burning your pa and every one in it!"

The defenders raised screams of joy as they saw the brightening glare in the sky. The Manianga men gathered into a group, then there came the drumming of a hundred pairs of feet, followed by the crackle and rustle of trampled ferns and bushes dying away into the distance.

"The Tere-Moana are good friends indeed," said the Motu chief. "But this running away of the Manianga taua might be only a ruse. They may sneak back. We'll repair our defences and wait for dawn before we send off a scout to see what's happened."

All through the rest of the night, fear clutching coldly at their hearts, the Manianga warriors ran towards their home. As the first exhausted men staggered out of the forest groans of dismay burst from them. Nothing remained of their splendid pa except charred stumps and heaps of ashes from which smoke still rose.

Down by the gardens, huddled in wailing groups, were the old men, the women, and the children. A short distance away, ringed by armed guards, were the few fighting-men left alive.

"Throw down your weapons and beg for mercy!" Maui said sternly. "Otherwise . . ." He gestured with his carved club towards the hostages.

Weary and sick at heart, their feet and legs torn and bleeding from that desperate, night-long run, the Manianga advance-guard surrendered. So did the rest of their men as they straggled in. Their women were allowed to bring them water, then Maui addressed them.

"We told you our mana was too strong for you to have any hope of beating us, but you ignored our warning. You attacked our friends the Motu without cause." He gestured towards the burnt-out pa.

"Again you pay a heavy penalty. You intended to attack us after you'd killed all the Motu. Now you'll suffer the fate you've often inflicted on others. You'll be hunted into poor country, there to live as best you can. But take warning. If you ever attack us again we'll exterminate you!"

They were allowed to rest for the remainder of the day, while their women gathered fern root and cooked it to feed them. That night they slept under guard. Late in the afternoon a panting Motu scout arrived. Maui told him what had happened, then pointed to the ruins of the pa.

"You can rebuild it when the warm weather returns." He indicated the surrounding country with a sweep of his arm. "This land will now belong to your people. It has fine soil for gardens and good spots for fishing along the coast. We hand it over to the Motu as a reward. All we ask is that some friends of ours, new arrivals from Tahiti-Nui, be allowed to settle on the eastern end of this country. Then we shall live as neighbours, growing too great and strong for any to dare to attack us."

In the morning the scout hurried away to take the good news to his people, and the Manianga were ordered to march. For three days the defeated tribe was shepherded along valleys and over hills; then they reached a divide overlooking a country of stunted scrub, with few creeks and a hungry soil of pumice sand.

"Your new land. Don't dare to leave it!" said Maui.

After the Tere-Moana warriors had marched away the Manianga women began to abuse their menfolk. The wrinkled old widow of the chief who had led their fathers to death at the battle of the fish-net was especially bitter. The young men listened in sulky silence for a time, then

one stood up and went among the others. Some wouldn't
heed what he said, but a few agreed.

"What are you going to do?" demanded the chief's
widow.

"Exact utu vengeance," replied the young man, his face
set and his tone bitter. "We'll all die doing it, but that's
better than living with our mana lost—and, what is even
worse, condemned to listen to the reproaches of the old
women who brought us up to indulge in the folly of attacking the powerful, cunning Tere-Moana a second time."

With stones chipped to cutting edges they turned short,
heavy sticks into makeshift weapons, then set off along the
route taken by Maui's taua, heedless of the wails of their
wives or the cries of the old women, who now tried to call
them back.

When Maui awakened next morning he huddled inside
his cloak, for the air in the hills was chilly. He thought
happily of the triumphant homecoming of his taua, bringing news that the Manianga had been broken. With peace
assured, they could now refit that Tahitian canoe, and a
dozen or so of them could pay a visit to their Hawaiki.

In his mind he pictured the island rising out of the sea
ahead of the canoe, the crowd gathering on the beach to
welcome them. How Kura would enjoy eating bananas
again and drinking the sweet water from green coconuts!
He thought of the cries of wonder from the people as they
listened to the story of the voyage to Aotearoa and the
many adventures there.

They would take a gift of many large pieces of pounama
stone. He would see his father, mother, and his boyhood
friend Tatau again. It was unlikely that old Hikurangi
would still be living. . . . On the return trip they could
bring more of their people to this new land, with pigs,
fowls, banana plants. . . .

His daydreams were shattered by a shout from a sentry
and a rush of naked figures from the tall, dew-wet bracken

fern beside the camp. Maui seized his club, tried to spring up, but was tripped by the cloak which he had tucked around his feet. One of the suicidal Manianga attackers recognized him and sprang forward.

"Where's your mana now?" he yelled, as he brought the heavy stick down with both hands on Maui's head.

For a few moments the camp was a scene of confusion, then it formed into groups, each striking at an attacker. Shouts of triumph echoed along the valley as the last Manianga warrior was felled; then a cry of consternation drew the Tere-Moana men to where one figure lay.

In a dazed silence they gathered around the body of their leader, unable to credit that he was one of the five men killed on their side. Maui, hero of the battle of the fishing-net; Maui, their daring scout and cunning leader of fighting-men, slain by a Manianga armed with nothing better than a heavy stick, because his legs had been tangled in his cloak!

Strange and terrible were the fortunes of war, thought Hauka, who was second-in-command, as he looked down at the body of his dead friend. There would be no triumphant homecoming now. . . .

Some of the men clamoured for the entire Manianga tribe to be wiped out as a reprisal. Others, in a fit of blind rage, struck again at the bodies of the attackers. Finally Hauka called for silence.

"We can't go back to exact utu from the Manianga," he told them. "We're nearly out of food, and there's nothing to eat in the country through which we have passed. We must be content with having killed those fifteen men."

He looked around. "Dig a grave beside that tree for our dead. As for those who attacked us"—he kicked savagely at the nearest corpse—"we'll scatter their bones!"

When the Tere-Moana taua returned, silent and downcast, Kura at first refused to believe that her brave, handsome, clever Maui was dead. "He's gone away before and he's always come back," she said hoarsely, gazing into the distance. But at last she bowed her head and broke into the tangi wails of mourning.

Ruapara came to see her when her grief had dulled. His hair seemed a lot greyer and the lines on his face deeper, for he mourned both his sons, also killed in that dawn attack.

"You will come into my house," he said to Kura, then he gazed thoughtfully at the sturdy, bright-eyed Perere. Although still a child, the boy was showing the signs of the born leader. In their play older lads deferred to him.

"I shall bring up your first-born to succeed me, Kura. He shows promise of being just as wise and brave as his father was."

13

THE VOYAGES OF PERERE

Perere's resemblance to his mother became more marked when he grew up. He had the same heavy build, thick eyebrows, and square chin. Like her, he showed great skill at handicrafts. But in character he took more after his father, having the ability to think things out for himself and the self-confidence so necessary in one destined to become a chief.

He had also inherited Maui's urge to travel. Aided by six other enterprising young men, he built a canoe big enough to carry seven people and all their gear, with a high freeboard to enable it to make deep-sea voyages. In it they sailed up and down the coast, landing on small and uninhabited islands whenever they had to rest and renew their supplies of food and water or to overhaul the canoe.

From these voyages Perere would return to keep the people entertained with accounts of what he had seen. Among other things he was able to report that a few more canoes bringing emigrants had arrived from Tahiti-Nui, Rangiatea, and Rarotonga. Many babies were being born, too. As a result the northern tip of Aotearea was becoming thickly populated. In some places the villages were only a few hours' walk apart.

Most of the people whom he met were very friendly. They welcomed him for two things; his party always brought a great deal of news, and Perere himself had become quite famous as a singer. He had a voice of great range and power.

When he sang a war, working, or marching chant people

hundreds of paces away could hear it quite distinctly, yet he could also sing love songs, in a voice scarcely audible outside the whare in which he sat, but with such tenderness that maidens trembled and looked at the ground.

He wouldn't visit some villages, however. He would order his men to cease paddling while still some distance from the shore and talk to the crowd on the beach across the intervening stretch of water, but would refuse all invitations to land there.

"They look too much like those untrustworthy, murderous Manianga," he would tell his crew, when they were paddling away.

There came a trip when he ventured farther than on any previous voyage, to round the Te Reinga cape at the northern end of Aotearoa and sail down the west coast. Here he found no islands lying off shore, few harbours in which a landing could be made, and long stretches of beach on which broke a heavy surf.

He had almost decided to put about, when smoke was sighted ahead, and they sailed on to find a large, landlocked bay. They had to wait until high water before they could enter, for there was a bar across the entrance.

They located the source of the smoke at a camp where twelve men were repairing a twin-hulled, ocean-going canoe. Perere hailed them, saying his party came in peace; the others replied in a friendly tone, but they spoke in a strange dialect. It was some time before either party could make out what the other was trying to convey.

"Our Hawai'i is Lanai," said the leader of the strangers, pointing in a direction a little east of north. The term 'Hawai'i' puzzled Perere, until he realized it was 'Hawaiki', with one of the sounds in the word replaced by a catch in the breath. Further questions revealed that Lanai must lie at a great distance, for they spoke of calling in at several intervening islands on the trip, all many days' sail apart.

"Your homeland must be right at the end of the world!"

Perere cried, after adding up the time in days which they had spent on the voyage.

He looked at the wood in their canoe. It was a light-yellow timber which he had never seen previously, and it had a strange, sweet smell when cut. Unfamiliar also was the dark wood in their paddles, the feather headdresses they carried in a hollow wooden tube to protect them from the damp, and the designs carved upon their clubs.

Presently Huloa, their leader, showed Perere his greatest treasures, kept on a shelf below the steering platform. They were frames of thin sticks, lashed together in what looked like a haphazard way, with sea-shells tied to them here and there.

"These enable us to find our way around the great ocean," Huloa explained. "Look at this one. Here is our homeland at the top end. These sticks show how the waves run on the voyage south to Kahiki." This place-name mystified Perere, until he realized it was how Huloa pronounced Tahiti.

"These other sticks show the directions from which the winds blow during the voyage, while the shells mark the islands where people are friendly and allow us to land. We bring them gifts of coloured feathers, and they make us presents of food and water."

Perere was enthralled. Those stick frames were a wonderful idea! Now he understood how Huloa could find his way home again. "What brings you so far from your Hawaiki?" he inquired.

"I'm the first-born of a great chief. I go out to see the world and gain wisdom from those I meet, as you learned about these charts from me."

Perere looked at where some of Huloa's crew were shaping up a new crossbeam for their canoe. "Now I'll give you a surprise," he said. From his canoe he took three adzes with pounamu blades. "Let your men try these," he suggested.

"Where do you get the stone which looks so beautiful and cuts so keenly?" Huloa inquired. "Some of it would be a treasure to take home with me."

Perere told him where it was found, then invited him to visit the Tere-Moana pa. "We'll make you a present of some pounamu," he promised.

Huloa was very interested in the offer, but explained that he still had some exploring to do. "No man knows what lies there," he said, pointing to the west. "I want to sail that way before I visit your people." He glanced at Perere's men.

"Why not come with us? You have six good seamen. I'm shorthanded. Eight of my crew decided to stay at Kahiki, where food is plentiful and the girls are very beautiful. My men took wives from among them and said they'd spend the rest of their lives there."

Perere was keen to grasp this opportunity, but what was to become of his smaller but fine canoe? He couldn't leave it here to rot or to be appropriated by the next people who visited this bay. Huloa provided the simple and obvious solution. He measured the length and beam of Perere's craft with a stick, then waded out to where his big double canoe was anchored.

"See! If you dismantle your outrigger it can be slipped inside one hull of my craft, but will still leave a space for us to bail out water."

Perere turned to his men. "We'll sail with Huloa. Catch fish with our dragnet, gut them, and hang them on strings to dry, as food for the voyages."

Twelve days later the canoe crossed the bar and a course was laid for the west. Huloa had the material for making additional charts, and he now started one for this voyage into unknown seas. Perere watched what he did. One side of the frame represented the western coast of Aotearoa, with a shell to mark the inlet from which they had sailed. Sticks tied across at an angle showed that the waves ran from the south-west. As they sailed westward another stick was added each day to show the wind direction. Then came the evening when Huloa stood in the bows, threw back his head, and cried, "I smell land!"

Perere sniffed at the wind. It did carry a faint, strange tang! At dawn they sighted tara-tara land birds gliding over the waves and diving occasionally to pick up a small fish. Beyond them, as the light grew, appeared the dim blue line of the coast. "It must be a great land," Huloa commented.

By sunset they were quite close, and could see that the hills inland were clothed with trees. After dark a cluster of red dots appeared, glowing and twinkling against a black background. "People live here," said Huloa. "There's the lights of a village." They took down the sail, put out a spar for a sea anchor, and let the canoe drift for the night.

Dawn found them off a forbidding line of cliffs, with surf breaking at their foot. Columns of smoke rose inland. "Those aren't cooking fires," said Perere, his thick eyebrows knitted in a puzzled frown. After a time he saw other smokes go up. "They seem to be signals," he commented.

The canoe sailed north, parallel to the coast, with the smoke columns continuing to spring up. At last a bay appeared, and they paddled into it. Many dark-brown figures came into view over the sandhills, carrying long spears.

"They seem a savage folk," said Huloa. "Still, we must land to renew our food and water. Let's look for a place easy to defend."

They found it on the north side of the bay, in the form of a small, scrub-clad cape, connected to the mainland by a narrow spit of sand, bare except for a few bushes. Here they came across signs of human habitation in the form of a mound of ashes, bones and shells, rude bough huts, stones chipped to cutting edges, and a small well of fresh water.

They camped for two days on the cape, and there was no sign of the natives of the country, except for the signal smokes inland. Finally Perere's curiosity overcame his caution, and he went off to explore, carrying a club and a fighting-lance. It was indeed a strange land. The trees had sheets of loose bark clinging to their trunks, and their long, thin leaves had a pungent smell when crushed. The birds were new to him, especially the cockatoos, which flew in large flocks with raucous cries. He was full of news when he returned.

"I saw a large bird which cannot fly, like our moa. But the animal I saw! The same colour as a kiore rat, it stands upright like a man and just as tall. It has a dog's head and a tail shaped like an eel. It did not run away—it hopped on its hind-legs, with its feet side by side, as does a tree-living bird!"

"When we return to Lanai our people won't believe such things!" said Huloa.

"That happened with me when I first went off exploring," said Perere, grinning at the memory. "Why didn't you bring back a leaf, a bone, or a tail-feather?" they used to say. "So then I did bring home specimens."

"I'll do it!" Huloa cried, picking up a basket. Perere took another one. Into them they packed some of the tree-leaves with the strong scent, brightly coloured feathers which birds had dropped, and a few of the crude stone implements.

The mound of ashes and food refuse yielded other specimens, including legs of the moa-like bird and two skulls of the animals which hopped on their hind-legs.

"Keep that basket out of sight when you return to your Hawaiki," Perere advised. "Tell your stories and wait for your people to scoff. Then produce your basket and ask them to tell you what the things are. Watch the silly look on their faces!"

The crew worked hard at netting and drying fish, for the

smoke columns were now moving closer. Distant voices were heard in the scrub, then all was silent, but the behaviour of the birds in the trees on the far side of the sand-spit told Perere that men were hidden there and spying on them.

Next day a line of men with heads of tousled hair, big beards, and white stripes painted on their dark bodies emerged from the trees and stood staring across the sand-spit. All carried very long spears.

Perere shouted friendly words, but the dark men replied in a strange tongue. Its angry tone made its meaning clear, however; it was a challenge to fight. Suddenly one plucked something from his string belt and flung it. Like a bird it flew through the air, passed overhead with a *hu-hu-hu* sound, hovered for an instant, then came gliding back, to bury half its length in the sand with a vicious *thup!*

Perere pulled it out. It was as long as his arm, as broad as three fingers, thin, sharp-edged, curved like the new moon, and made from some very hard and heavy wood. Never had he imagined a weapon capable of striking you from behind!

"These may be deadly warriors!" he said uneasily.

"We'd better pack up and go!" Huloa said.

Before anyone could move to obey, one of the dark-skinned men fitted the butt of a spear to a flat piece of wood and swung it. The spear left it, sailed across, and Huloa had to dodge to avoid being transfixed. Then more spears came curving through the air, aimed with a most disconcerting accuracy.

One of the men from Lanai snatched up a spear and threw as hard as he could, but it fell less than half-way. "Fool!" Huloa snarled. "Now they know we can't hit back!"

Perere saved the day. Under the cover of some bushes he stuck the butt-end of one of the savage men's spears into the sand, its wickedly barbed point towards the enemy. With Huloa's fighting-staff and a piece of fishing-line he improvised a whip of the type used by the Motu tribe to throw the kotaha dart, hitched the free end of the cord to the spear shaft, and put all his strength into the cast.

Luck was with him. Usually a kotaha could not be thrown with any accuracy, but this spear shot over the tops of the bushes and dropped straight for the line of brown men. One had to duck to avoid being struck in the head. For a moment the savages stood still, then they uttered yells of dismay and raced into the cover of the trees.

"They'll be back when they get over that surprise," Huloa forecast. "Put everything into the canoe! Never mind those fish that aren't dry yet. We've got to get away!"

As they paddled out to sea the yelling savages swarmed on to the end of the little cape, and one flung a spear after the canoe. As soon as the sail had been set, Huloa looked around. "Anything left behind?" he inquired.

"Yes!" growled Perere. "That curved wooden thing they threw at us. I wanted it to prove one of my stories, too.

Still, I have my basket of specimens and two of their spears."

One of Huloa's men gave a cry of dismay. "I left my spare adze-blades," he said. "I put them under a bush for safe keeping——"

"And now those savages will appreciate your gift!" Huloa said sarcastically. He was wrong on that point, however, although he never knew it. Strangely enough, the keen-eyed aborigines didn't notice them, drifting sand covered them, and there they lay hidden for hundreds of years until European settlers discovered them.

"That's one country our people will never colonize," said Perere, as the hostile coast was left behind. "Those dark people know how to guard it." He looked at the spears which he was taking home. "Wish I knew how they use a piece of flat wood to throw these things so far and accurately. It'd be a good way to drive off attackers."

"It's a most unsporting way to fight," Huloa commented. He took out his latest stick chart. "Steer that way," he said to the helmsman, pointing. "We must see if any islands lie north-east from here."

Four days later the look-out man sighted tara-tara birds, then the clouds which hung over the island on which they roosted. After a time the summits of two tall mountains crept into view above the horizon. They lay-to off the island that night, and at dawn sailed into a sheltered lagoon.

There were no footmarks on its beaches, and no smoke could be seen. When Perere landed to scout around he found the waterhens, pigeons, and other birds tame and inquisitive. He returned to the coast and reported the island to be uninhabited.

"That's good," said Huloa. "This snug anchorage will give us the opportunity to beach the canoe and overhaul it. I don't like the way the left-hand hull is leaking."

14

KURA DREAMS

Kura's heart was heavy with grief. Last year Perere, her first-born, had gone off on another of his trips, and since then nothing had been heard of him. She tried not to abandon hope, but it was only too likely that he was one more of the canoe voyagers who would never return.

Now Turongo, her youngest child, was doomed to be a cripple for the rest of his life. It had happened so simply. He had scrambled down the path leading from the pa to the ledge at the foot of the bluff where he kept his little fishing-canoe. That route had been left rough to hinder any enemies who came by water and tried to use it.

Half-way there was a jutting boulder on which people had trodden hundreds of times, but it came loose when Turongo stepped on it. As he fell to the ledge below it rolled after him, to smash his ankles and crush both feet.

The broken bones had knitted, but now his feet and ankles were as stiff and as immovable as if carved from wood. Unable to move except with a clumsy hobble, he could no longer play games, dance, or work in the gardens. It strengthened Kura's love for him—but it looked as if he could never be anything except a very humble person in the tribe.

Sad-eyed, she went out to see what he was doing. She found him with a broad piece of totara wood which had been split from a log and adzed flat. He was drawing a design on it with the point of a shark tooth. He glanced up at her and said, "If I can do nothing else I might become a great woodcarver."

Kura became aware of a dawning hope. Wood-carving was a most honourable occupation! Even a high chief did not think it beneath his dignity to use the mallet of whalebone, the stone chisel, and the fish-tooth graver on ornamenting a canoe figurehead or a doorpost for a house. She stooped to study the sketched lines.

"It's good—but a bit uneven," she commented. "I'll show you how a woman lays out a weaving pattern." She fetched her little measuring-sticks and used them to square up the drawing. When the layout was finished she inquired, "What goes in the centre?"

Somewhat diffidently he showed what he had drawn on the inner surface of a piece of bark. Kura stared at the grotesque face, with its sly eyes, grinning mouth, and protruding tongue. "I tried to copy the expression a warrior wears when he performs the haka war-dance," Turongo explained.

"I've never seen anything like it!" she cried. "It's quite new!" She wondered how she could help him. It was tapu for a woman to go near a woodcarver while he was working, or even to look upon the task until it was completed. . . . She glanced at his kit of tools.

I

"I'll fetch you the pipi shells with broken edges you'll need for the final scraping," she offered.

Turongo's design soon attracted the attention of the men, but at first their criticism was destructive. Why go in for new ideas? Weren't the patterns which had been handed down for generations good enough for him? When the carving was finished and put on show the women were hostile.

"This hideous thing will scare the children into fits!" one exclaimed. There was a murmur of agreement. Turongo stood it for a time, then suggested that somebody try it out by letting a youngster see it. A woman went away and returned with a two-year infant.

The plump child which she carried stared at the carving with round eyes, then held out its arms to it with a chuckle of "goo-ga!" Then it did cry, but only because it was scared by the roar of laughter from the men.

Ruapara delivered the final judgment. "In this new land we do many things unknown in our Hawaiki," he said. "On the island where we older people were born nobody sat over a fire to keep warm. Here we do it for half the year. There we had no windbreaks around garden plants. Here they die without them. There our houses had no walls, so the cool air could blow through them. Here we have to shut out the cold winds."

He scrutinized the carving again.

"It's the same with Turongo's work. New designs are proper in a new land. This young man has great skill. He shall do another one to match this; then they'll be used as doorposts in my own house."

Kura gave thanks to Tane, god of the craftsmen, as she listened. With Perere lost, she would never be a high chief's honoured mother now, but at least she would have a noted artist for a son. It would mean a lot to Turongo too. In spite of being a cripple he could still have a career.

She now realized there was little chance of seeing her

Hawaiki again. The fine canoe owned by the Tahitians had been stolen by a raiding party from a northern tribe one night as it lay at anchor off the village which the new-comers were building.

If he had lived to become chief in succession to Ruapara some day, Perere would have been able to order the building of an ocean-going canoe in which the voyage could be made, but that hope had also gone now. . . .

Only the survivors of those who had manned the *Tere-Moana* canoe had any desire to visit that far-off birthplace, but now they were beginning to say that they were too old to face the risks and hardships of so long a voyage. . . .

But memories of her Hawaiki continued to come while Kura slept. Often in her dreams she was there again, hearing the rumble of the surf on the reef and the palm leaves rattling in the wind, while the soft, moist air caressed her skin. . . .

One day she resolved to make a last appeal to the gods for the return of her Perere. She went to a spot on the head of the bluff, where a rock shelf made a natural seat, and there she sat for hour after hour, staring towards the north, whispering her prayer again and again.

At that moment, on an island many days' sail away, Perere was looking at a huge piece of timber in the forest, surrounded by an ankle-deep litter of chips. The new canoe hull was nearing completion at last. His mind went back to the day, nearly a year previously, when they had beached their canoe here, under the impression that only a small leak had to be caulked.

Instead they had made the appalling discovery that the bottoms of both hulls had been riddled by some kind of sea worm. "It's a wonder it didn't sink under us," Huloa had said. "We must be under the special protection of Tangaroa and Hine-Moana."

Only one thing could save them from being marooned on this island for the rest of their days; they must build another craft. It was decided that Perere's canoe, decked over except for a small bailing well amidships, would serve for the smaller of the twin hulls, but the larger one would have to be made from the biggest tree they could find within hauling distance of the water.

As they had only five adzes among them and the spare blades had been lost, they had to make additional tools. They tried to live under makeshift shelters, but a man couldn't do a good day's work when he had been kept awake at night by water dripping on him, so three weeks had to be spent on building and thatching a weathertight house.

Then there was the matter of food. Fish had to be caught, birds snared, shellfish gathered, and wild vegetables found. When food was brought home it wouldn't cook itself, so this involved more work. So did the gathering of firewood. It meant that only ten men of their party of nineteen could work on the making of the new canoe. The rest were kept busy on finding and preparing food for all hands.

Then Oatani, the man who had left the spare adze-heads behind in the great western land, and who was their expert woodworker, had his leg ripped by a sting-ray spine while he was helping to spear fish by torchlight one night. He was laid up for a long time by a wound which refused to heal.

On the evening of the day when he had been thinking over these things Perere was unable to sleep. First he worried about his chance of becoming chief of the tribe if he returned after so long an absence. Would Ruapara have adopted another son, believing him to be dead?

Now he understood his mother's longing to see her Hawaiki again. How he wished he was back in the pa where he had been born! After a time his thoughts centred on his mother. She probably mourned him as dead. If only he could let her know that he was still alive and well!

Abruptly he recalled part of his initiation into the mysteries. Ruapara had told him that a very wise Tohunga priest, versed in the secret lore and rendered skilful by self-discipline, could send thought-messages to another Tohunga living on an island many days' sail away.

Perere wondered if he could do the same thing now with Kura. Surely a mother and son could be as much in sympathy with each other as any priests? Ruapara had said you must have a dire need for sending such a message to have any chance of success. You must also have a firm belief in your power to accomplish it.

"I'm certainly longing to assure my mother that all is well," Perere said to himself.

He rose from his bed of leaves, clad in his worn, soiled cloak, and went to a spot where he could look across the sea. After studying the stars he was able to face the direction of Aotearoa. He sat down and began to concentrate on the first step of thinking of Kura until he had a clear picture of her in his mind.

He recalled her big, dark eyes under their thick brows, her rare but beautiful smile, the fond expression on her broad face when she looked at her children. He imagined himself a child at her knee again, listening while she told the story of the voyage in the *Tere-Moana* canoe and of how she had steered the craft while the men were helpless from exhaustion.

Tears brimmed his eyes as he recalled other childhood memories: Kura washing his grubby face and hands, showing him how to find shellfish, teaching him to swim.... He thought of her at her weaving-frame, making clothes for her family. How bitter had been her tangi wailing when she had learned of Maui's death....

Now Perere was staring into the darkness, sweat standing in beads on his face with the intensity of the effort as he tried to send her a thought-message saying that he was alive and would return as soon as he could. He repeated it in his mind until he was giddy from the effort, then stumbled back to the camp and fell into an exhausted sleep.

He felt strangely cheerful as he hacked away with an adze next morning. He told Huloa what he had done, but he worked as he talked. "Prayers are all right," he remarked, "but you have to work so they can be granted."

"That's what I think," his friend agreed. "When a storm overtakes my canoe I tell my crew to pray to the gods—but not to stop bailing for a moment!"

In the pa far away Kura was also cheerful that morning. "I dreamed of my first-born last night," she said to Ngaio. "He's on an island. It's a place I've never heard described. Part is level and covered with trees. It has two mountains. One has a flat top and the other a peak. Their heads are sometimes hidden in clouds.

"Perere is there with his own men and some who seem strangers. I saw them using adzes. They must be making a new canoe, for chips lay everywhere. My ariki son isn't lost. He'll come back to me."

Until the night of this dream Kura had often taken her missing son's possessions out of their wrappings and had cried over them. "Where are you hidden, my ariki, my first-born?" she had sobbed. "Oh, that you would walk in again through the door!" But now she set to work on weaving a fine feather cloak.

"He'll need it when he returns," she told the daughters who assisted with the task. "In my dream he wore a thing so tattered you wouldn't use it for a floormat!"

Sitting in a workshop which was tapu to women and working away at the second carving, Turongo hoped his mother was right. He couldn't believe that his big strong, handsome brother was dead. He longed to show him the carved slabs.

"See," he planned to say. "I can still do a man's work!"

Ruapara was very interested in Kura's dream about her

missing son. He asked many questions. Finally he said, "Perere is still alive, but he has yet to make a safe voyage home. Continue to pray for his return."

Before long the chief had to concentrate on a very serious problem. A messenger arrived from their allies the Motu. The Manianga hadn't stayed long in those barren hills to which they had been driven. Moving on, they had come to good country on the west coast. Here they had joined forces with another tribe, which had fine gardens, good fishing-grounds, and forests containing an abundance of birds.

These new allies had attacked a small peaceful tribe living to the north of them, making slaves of the survivors, one of whom had escaped, bringing the news that the Manianga planned to march across the hills and exact a terrible utu vengeance from the Tere-Moana people.

"Their old women have never forgotten those insulting remarks about the cloaks they made. They still upbraid their young men because the tribe has suffered two defeats," the ex-slave had reported.

It was Turongo who made the best suggestion. "Send a spy among them. Let my mother weave a cloak with a new pattern in it—one nobody has seen before. When it is finished people must walk over it until it looks worn and old. I'll carve the same patterns on a club for him to carry. Train him well for the part he must play."

"Your father lives again in you," Ruapara said approvingly.

"Unfortunately, I can't go on this mission myself," Turongo added, looking down at his club feet.

"My youngest son, Makatiti, is brave and wise," said Hauka. "He longs for an opportunity to distinguish himself. Give him the task."

Makatiti was given a very thorough training before he was sent off. He had to claim he was a survivor from a tribe which had been attacked by the Tere-Moana. He

longed to be revenged. Over and over again he rehearsed
his story.

Determined to leave nothing to chance, other men
would accost Makatiti without warning, demanding to
know who he was and where he came from. They told him
where his tale seemed unconvincing. They would also
awaken him at night, asking the same questions, to see if
he would give himself away by an incautious remark.

At last Ruapara was satisfied. "Go on your mission," he
directed. That night—the Manianga might have had
watchers posted in the hills which overlooked the Tere-
Moana country—a most convincing fugitive, wearing a
tattered cloak, stole out of the pa under cover of the darkness and headed westward.

A fortnight later the Manianga leader and his chief fighting-men watched a famished, ragged stranger wolf the
food which they had placed before him. They listened to
his story and subjected him to a searching cross-examina-
tion. They looked at the scar on his forehead, actually the
mark of a fall when Makatiti was a child, but resembling
that inflicted by the thrust of a fighting-lance.

"We'll think over what you've told us," they said. They
waited until the exhausted man had fallen asleep, then
awakened him roughly and shouted questions before his
mind had cleared.

"It is well," the Manianga high chief said at last. "The
gods must be on our side, otherwise this fellow would not
have come to us. With him as a guide our victory over the
Tere-Moana is assured."

15

MOON MAIDEN

The new canoe which Huloa, Perere, and their companions had built with so much labour had been baptized, named, and given a trial. Now it lay moored close to the shore, as graceful as a gull resting on the water. The men were engaged on the final task of preparing food for the voyage. Perere, his expression downcast, went to where Huloa was making the frame for a new chart.

"It's a pity we cannot sail straight back to my home," he said.

Huloa pointed to the chart. "See for yourself. At this time of the year the winds around this part of the great ocean blow from the south-east. These sticks indicate it. But over here, on the Ara-Moana sea-path which one follows from Tahiti to Aotearoa, they blow from the northeast. Only the gods know why winds blow in what seems such contrary ways.

"No need for me to tell you that a canoe cannot sail into the wind. To get to your home, therefore, we must first let this south-east wind carry us over there." He pointed to the middle of the frame. "When we reach it we will find a wind which will take us down here, where your home lies." He pointed to the bottom right corner of the chart, then paused to think of some appropriate simile.

"It is like coming to a bog on which you cannot tread. To get to the other side you must walk around it."

Perere agreed with a gloomy nod. It was as Huloa said. But it meant that a long time must pass before they would sail into the bay where his people lived.

A few days later, when they were sailing away from the island on which they had been marooned so long, Perere looked back at it. Only the summits of the two mountains were now visible.

"There's a thing that puzzles me," he said. "Why does the highest part of an island come into view first as you near it and is the last to be seen as you sail away?"

"Our wise old men say the world must be curved," Huloa replied.

"Then why doesn't the sea run down the slope to the edges, leaving dry land only in the middle?"

"That's known to the gods alone."

Presently Perere reached for some chart-making materials. "I'll make a map of the world, with all the places you know of marked with shells. It'll help me to tell my story when I'm back with my people, just as a stick with notches on the edge aids you to remember the names of your ancestors."

"My folk use a knotted cord to help them remember," Huloa remarked.

Perere made the frame of his chart. "We'll begin with your homeland," he said. "I'll put it here, up in the northeast corner, for it must be near the end of the world."

"No, there is another land much farther off. Some of my ancestors sailed to it, guided by little yellow birds which came from it every year, to fly home again six moons later. There live people with skins the colour of ripe plantains. Great trees grow there. Logs from them float across the sea to my homeland. We build our big canoes from them."

Perere decided not to put it on his chart. The frame would be crowded now with the many places which he had to mark on it. It took days to memorize the stories which Huloa had to tell about all the islands represented by shells tied to the sticks. Then came a dawn when the look-out man sighted land birds.

"Ahead is another island," said Huloa. "It lies on our course, so we'll be able to see what it's like."

The land rose into view at noon. When they skirted it in search of a landing-place late in the afternoon they saw a hilly island on which were tall, straight trees with the branches growing in rings on their trunks.

Sailing around the island convinced them that a landing could be made in one place alone, and then only when the wind blew off shore. "We'll have to haul the canoe up on those shelving rocks, too," said Huloa. "Otherwise it'll be wrecked if the wind blows from this side."

They landed at dawn next morning. After hauling the canoe to a safe place they set off to explore the island. They had thought it to be uninhabited, as no smoke had been sighted, but a shout soon called them together at a spot where some edible roots had been dug up. Then they sighted a large log which was being turned into a canoe.

"Only one man appears to be working on it," said Perere. "He's been at it a long time. Look how old these chips are in the bottom layer around it."

Moving on, they came to paths trodden in the grass, but nobody answered their hails. They split into four parties and tramped over the island, exploring all the ferny gullies and crawling into every thicket of scrub. Signs of human beings were quite common. One of the Maori men found a long, dark, woman's hair caught on a stick. Another found several hairs lighter in colour with a rippling wave in them.

They discovered footprints, two sets belonging to children. They saw where stone tools had been chipped into shape. But of the people they didn't catch a glimpse. "Why isn't there smoke?" said one man, when they returned to the canoe at dusk. "How can they cook without fire?"

"The legends of my people tell of the Manahune, a shy little folk who lived in the forests," said Huloa, glancing around uneasily. "They were said to work evil spells if you offended them."

"All the footprints I've seen were the usual size," Perere pointed out. "These must be ordinary people. I'd like to solve this puzzle."

"We can rest here for a few days," suggested a Maori. They occupied their time in fishing. At intervals one would shout, "We are friends. Come to visit us." But nobody appeared. Perere stretched some very fine threads of palm leaf across two of the paths and found one broken next day. These people were spying on his party from cover; that was plain.

"I know how we might get them to come out," said Huloa. "Let's take our adzes and make them a present of a day's work on their canoe." The party set to work with a will, making a big impression on the hollowing of the log. At intervals Perere's powerful voice rang out in a shout of "See how we labour for you! Doesn't it show we're friends?" But still there was no sign of the people of the island.

It took Perere a long time to get to sleep that night. Finally an idea came to him. Next morning he said, "You others can go on fishing to-day. Leave this puzzle to me." One of Huloa's men had a very pretty feather headdress, and it was still in good condition, although it had been kept shut up for a long time.

Perere took it and set off along the path which had been most used. It led to a creek, where it ended. Perere had already surmised that those using it walked in the water from this point to hide their tracks, and he had followed the creek to its source at a spring in some boulder-strewn ground, but had failed to find where the people left the water.

He now sat down at the point where the path ended and lit a fire, piling on green boughs to raise a big smoke. That should make those people curious, he thought. Then

he raised his voice in a marching song. That should excite
their curiosity still further. Finally he stuck a forked stick
into the ground by the ashes of the fire and hung the headdress on it.

When he hurried to the spot next morning the headdress
had gone, and in its place was an armband neatly braided
from strips of palm leaf. Below it, and apparently put
there on purpose, was a girl's footprint in the damp ground.

Perere slipped the bangle on his left arm, sang the
marching song again, then his voice sank, and he began
the love-chant which he had composed while lying awake
on the previous night:

> "Your hair
> Waves like the tree-fern leaves.
> Your eyes
> Shine like stars by night.
> Your voice,
> Sweet as the song of the tui,
> Makes me burn with longing . . ."

When he ceased there was a lengthy silence, and then,
as elusive as a bird-call in the forest, a girl's voice replied.
He held out his arms in the direction from which it had
appeared to come and sang his new song again, but this
time there was no reply. Disappointed, he sat dejectedly
by the creek bank. Apparently the island girl was too timid
to show herself. . . .

A faint rustle made him look up, and he saw her at last.
She stood in the knee-deep water some twenty paces up-
stream, trembling and staring at him with wide eyes. Her
skin was a pale, clear brown, and the sunbeams, striking
through gaps in the foliage overhead, glinted on her wavy
hair.

Never had Perere seen a prettier creature. She stood
poised like some shy bird, ready for flight. Perere began
to sing the soft lullaby which his mother had used when

putting his sisters and brother to sleep. He took off the plaited armband, pressed it to his heart, and replaced it again.

"Did you like the pretty feather headdress I left for you?" he said gently.

"Yes!" she breathed. Her gaze went to Perere's bulging shoulder muscles, his deep chest, and his sturdy legs. She uttered a soft "Oo-oo" of admiration.

"I'm Perere, an ariki of the Tere-Moana people, who live in the great land of Aotearoa," he informed her.

"I'm Hine-Marama," she whispered.

She was well named, he thought. The Moon Maiden! She was indeed as fair as the moon on a warm summer night.

"Why did you bring all those other men with you, Perere? Why didn't you come alone?"

"A sailing-canoe must have a large crew to work it," he pointed out.

"I have prayed so often for your coming, Perere!" Her bearing was more confident now.

"I've dreamed of a maid like you, Marama! Never have

I seen one so beautiful!" She flushed and put up a hand to straighten her hair. "Do no men live on this island?" he inquired.

"Only my father. There are five of us. The others are my mother and sisters." She began to step backward. "I must go. They'll be anxious."

"You'll come here again?" he inquired eagerly.

"I'll be here in the morning," she promised.

"Tell your people not to fear us. We have come to help you. We invite your father to visit us."

She gave him a last, lingering glance, then flitted away.

Perere's companions were astonished at the news which he brought and broke into a chorus of questions. He told them to be patient. "I have no idea how they came here or where they hide. This girl is as shy as a huia bird. We mustn't scare her. I'll see her again in the morning."

Towards noon next day he returned to the camp, accompanied by a tall man with greying hair whose face and body were heavily tattooed. Although he was dressed in a plain kilt of palm-leaf strips, similar to that worn by his daughter Marama, his dignified bearing showed that he was a Rangatira.

"He is Meiva, a high chief from the far-off land of Nuka-Hiva," said Perere.

"You are welcome to my island," said Meiva.

Huloa hastened to serve the visitor with grilled fish and a gourd of drinking-water. For a time they exchanged greetings and good wishes; then Meiva told his story.

"There was a great battle on my island. The people from the adjoining valley attacked my tribe without warning. We were beaten. While I and my surviving fighting-men held off the enemy our women and children launched our big canoes and embarked. We made a last charge against our foes, drove them back, and swam out to the canoes before they could attack again."

He went on to relate how the canoes had sailed to another island, to be refused permission to land. Finally, in response to their pleas, a few men were allowed to go ashore and gather ripe coconuts for food. They met with similar rebuffs at other islands in the group. Then they sailed to the Tuamotu islands, only to meet with disaster.

Not knowing those waters, they found themselves trapped in a maze of coral reefs, with a storm approaching. Meiva's canoe managed to gain the open sea by hard paddling, but they didn't see any of the other craft again.

They made their way to the leeward side of one of the atolls, but again they were not allowed to land. The chief of the low island said that it was now overcrowded and there was no room for any more people there; the refugees would have to look for an island of their own. All he could do for them was to let them have some more coconuts.

"It was the same at all the other atolls," said Meiva. "Nobody wanted us to live with them. Finally I ordered the helmsman to steer south-west, hoping to find a new land somewhere."

After they had sailed for many days across the great Ocean-of-Kiwa, with never a sign of land, a great storm overtook them. The canoe began to break up, for it had been a long time at sea and there had been no chance to overhaul it.

Although they were familiar with tales of hardships on long canoe voyages, the story which followed outclassed anything which Meiva's audience had ever heard. When the canoe broke up Meiva and his wife had managed to swim to the outrigger float. They secured a basket which drifted past, to find it held fishing-lines and a stone knife, given to them at one of the islands. Meiva had loosened the lashings which secured the booms to the float and had tied the two free ends of the boom together, forming a triangle.

On this makeshift raft they had drifted day after day,

living on fish caught with the lines, rainwater from the thunder-squalls of the wet season, and an occasional coconut which they found floati.g. Finally, when reduced to little more than living skeletons, they had been cast ashore on this island.

"Here we've been ever since," said Meiva. "Here my daughters were born. They have never seen any other people until you came."

He glanced at the log on which he had been working. "When that canoe was finished I intended to embark my family and sail south-west. Land lies there. The birds which come and go each year showed me the course to steer. I hoped the people there would welcome us and my daughters would find husbands."

"It's lucky you didn't try it," Huloa said emphatically. "First you'd come to an island where nobody lives. Well do we know it—w 've just spent nearly a year there, making a new canoe. If you'd sailed on you would have come to the great land wl.ich lies on the western edge of the Ocean-of-Kiwa. Savage people live there. They would have killed you. We had to flee from them."

"But we'll take you to a new home," Perere told Meiva. "You'll live with my people. I'm heir to the high chief, so your welcome's assured. Now fetch your family to meet us. We'll sail as soon as this last lot of fish have dried."

The secret of the family's hiding-place was simple. On the face of one of the island's eastern cliffs was a roomy cave, reached by a rough path from the crest. The five islanders had avoided leaving tracks by stepping from boulder to boulder across the rock-strewn ground which lay between it and the creek. They had adopted this precaution in case hostile strangers landed.

"No wonder we couldn't find where you lived!" said Perere.

"We sighted your canoe when you sailed round the island," Meiva told him. "I watched what you did from

K

the shelter of the bushes after you landed. Then I ordered
my family to keep hidden until you left. We lived on shellfish which we gathered from the rocks at night." A smile
flitted across his tattooed face.

"But Marama disobeyed me. She went off in the daytime while I slept. There was a lure she couldn't resist."

"What was that, Chief?"

"Your singing, Perere!"

16

PERERE RETURNS

As he escorted Meiva's family to the camp by the beached canoe Perere felt an uneasy fear. For the first time in his life he had fallen in love. But what if the shy, beautiful Moon Maiden found one of those slim, handsome men from Lanai more to her liking?

He would fight to retain her, of course, and his six men would stand behind him—but they were outnumbered two to one by Huloa and his followers.

His fears were groundless. With a natural, unaffected dignity Marama took their frank stares of admiration their compliments, and their attentions for granted, but she had eyes for none of the others. Her gaze rested most often on Perere. How great was his strength—and yet how gentle he had been when he coaxed her to show herself! He is indeed the one of whom I've dreamed, she thought.

When they sailed she looked back at her birthplace through a mist of tears. Ever since she had been old enough to understand what her parents could tell her of the great world beyond the horizon she had longed to leave its isolation and mingle with other people. Now she realized how she loved the place.

"Never mind," Perere said consolingly. "I'm taking you where you'll never be lonely again. When I become chief of my people you will sit above all the other women!"

Marama kept him busy answering questions. He instructed her in the etiquette of his people. When they sighted the northern tip of Aotearoa he told her that the cape was named Te Reinga. From its crest the spirits of the dead set out on their journey to the world beyond.

"The country of my people lies a long way down the eastern coast of this great land," he informed her. "On the way to it we shall call in at the pa of some friends of mine. They'll welcome us and give us food for the remainder of the voyage. They are ruled by a woman, Wahine-Rona-Nui." He broke off to laugh.

"Well is she named 'Great Rona'! Never have I heard of a bigger woman! She is built like a whale! Her people revere her, though, for years ago her courage and fatness saved them. But that's a story she loves to tell herself."

The men from Lanai were not surprised to hear of a tribe ruled by a woman, for at home they had several female chiefs. But Meiva was incredulous. It was unheard of where he came from!

When the canoe sailed into the bay where Rona's people lived a great roar went up from the crowd on the beach as Perere was recognized. Marama stared, then sank into the canoe with a wail of dismay. Perere bent over her.

"They aren't angry," he assured her. "They are glad to see us. Stand up and let them look at the beautiful bride I'm taking home."

"It isn't that," she sobbed. Perere's thick eyebrows lowered in a bewildered frown. What could be wrong? Her mother and sisters were also cowering in the bottom of the canoe.

"Can't you see?" Marama said tearfully. "Why didn't you warn me?"

Perere looked at his companions. The other men were just as puzzled. Marama seized his hand. "Look at the fine clothes they wear! I can't go among them. I would be ashamed!"

Perere tried to reason with her. "What if you have only a palm-leaf skirt? Nobody expects women to wear fine cloaks when they land after a long voyage." But she and her mother, as well as the two young girls, refused to be convinced.

Perere realized that talk was useless. What could a man do? He saw the answer when his gaze alighted on the tool-kit. As soon as the anchor stone had been dropped he snatched up his best adze and jumped over the side. Running up the beach, he greeted the gigantic Rona-Nui by gripping both her hands and pressing his nose and forehead against hers in the hongi salutation; then he did the same with her two portly sons.

When etiquette left him free to do it he held out the adze. "We have a woman and three girls aboard," he explained. "We rescued them from an island far away, where nobody else lived except their father. I am betrothed to the eldest girl. But they would be shamed by coming among you wearing only leaf skirts while you have such beautiful feather capes. Will you exchange four cloaks for this?"

Rona's sons were astonished. Trade an adze with a pounamu blade for a few capes? They hurried Perere up to the pa, fearful that he would change his mind.

Perere selected garments which seemed of the right size, rolled them into a bundle, and waded back to the canoe. The tears stopped at once. "Now I can face those people!" said Marama, as she put on the feather headdress and stood up.

Perere felt a surge of pride as she stepped on the gunwale and he carried her ashore on his shoulder. There wasn't a more beautiful girl in Aotearoa!

When the strangers landed they stared at Rona. The woman chief was even larger than Perere had led them to believe! But Rona seemed proud of the sensation which her size caused. Puffing at every step, she led the way up to the pa.

While they waited for a feast to be prepared she listened to Perere's account of his adventures. Seeing how nervous and excited the three girls were, Rona placed them in the darkest corner of her house, with their parents sitting before them to shield them from the stares of those who had been invited to enter or who crowded around the doorway.

"If I were a man I'd sail off to see such things myself!" she cried, when Perere had related his latest experiences and had displayed his basket of curios.

"We understand you've had some great adventures in your time," said Meiva. "We'd like to hear of them."

"They happened when I was young," said Rona. "I've always been fat. Because of my great size no man courted me, although I was a chief's elder daughter. My ancestors brought banana plants from our Hawaiki. We kept them growing year after year by protecting them with high windbreaks.

"But the neighbouring tribe envied those banana plants and were angry because we wouldn't give them shoots so they could also grow some. They fell on us without any warning one very dark night. Most of our fighting-men were killed, including my father the chief and all my brothers.

"Burning torches were thrown over the palisade and set fire to the houses. Under cover of the smoke some of us broke a gap in the fence and ran to where our big canoes were kept. But when we reached them we found they wouldn't float." Rona paused and ran the gaze of her prominent black eyes over her attentive audience.

"The enemy had chopped a large hole in the bottom of every one!" she said dramatically.

"I jumped into the biggest canoe and blocked the hole by sitting on it! Only one as large as I could have done it! Aue! Those splinters! The pain I suffered!

"The men who were with us pushed off the canoe, and the women and children jumped aboard. They had to move it through the water by using clubs and hands. The enemy had taken all the paddles."

Rona went on to describe how she had to sit there for the next two days. Then they reached a small island where the men were able to patch the canoe with a sheet of bark and improvise a few paddles. "But I had to lie on my face under a tree," she chuckled. "Finally we reached this spot and made a new home here.

"More of our people who had survived the battle found their way to us, and we became a tribe again, but there was much quarrelling about who should now be chief. Finally I said, 'I'm the only Rangatira left alive. I'll lead the people.' They agreed, and I found a husband."

"I no longer marvel that this woman should be a chief," Meiva whispered to Perere.

"As we came up the path from the beach I saw that you still grow bananas," said Huloa.

"Yes. I was always longing to eat them again and mourning the plants we'd lost. Finally my husband went away, saying nothing of what he intended to do. He was gone for six days. I feared he was dead. Then he returned with some young banana plants. He had crept at night into our old pa, which the enemy had taken over, to get them." Rona sighed and big tears suffused her eyes.

"I'd thought he'd married me only because I was a chief, but after that I knew he really did love me. I cried for weeks when he died."

"My mother longs to eat bananas again," said Perere.

"I shall give you a bunch to take to her," Rona promised.

The voyagers stayed for three more days. Many men begged Perere to trade another pounamu-bladed adze. He drove a hard bargain, demanding a carved wooden box containing the feathers worn on ceremonial occasions, four more lightweight cloaks for Meiva's wife and daughters, and some fine sleeping-mats. There would be some ordinary flax kilts for him and the other men as well, of course. . . .

"There," he said to Marama, as he handed to her the best of the summer cloaks, the feather-box and the finest of the mats. "Now you won't enter the pa of my people without possessions. In fact, all the other girls will envy you."

Just before the canoe sailed on the last stage of the trip to the country of the Tere-Moana, Rona gave Perere a large package. "Keep them cool, so they won't ripen too soon," she directed.

Perere's heart thudded heavily as the canoe rounded the last cape and his well-remembered birthplace came into view. Gazing at the pa on its bluff, he wondered what changes had taken place during his absence. Had some other young man been chosen to succeed Ruapara as chief —or was the old man now dead and somebody ruling in his place?

He watched the stir as the canoe was sighted. He tried to recognize individuals among the crowd on the beach. Was that Kura standing apart from the rest—or was she in the centre of the big group? Was that Ruapara now walking over the sandhills? How slowly the canoe was moving!

Gradually the figures on the beach became plainer.

Suddenly the expected roar of welcome came across the water. Now he could see that Kura stood at a little distance from the others. He fidgeted impatiently, then called to the men at the paddles to double their efforts. Finally he flung off his cloak and dived over the side.

His powerful kau tawhai swimming stroke left the canoe behind. Panting heavily, he ran up the beach and gave his mother the hongi greeting. "E whaea! Did you fear I was dead?" he cried.

"E taku tama! I knew you lived. One night my spirit left my body as I slept. It journeyed to where you and some others made a new canoe. Then I stopped weeping. Instead I made this new cloak against your homecoming." She draped it over his massive shoulders.

The rest of the people had kept back while the mother greeted her long-lost son, but now they came forward, Ruapara at their head. After the salutes had been exchanged Perere handed the new cloak to his mother and waded out to where the canoe had dropped anchor. He returned carrying Marama.

"The maid I'm going to marry!" he shouted, holding the blushing girl up for all to see. "Her father's a Rangatira. Who'll receive him and his family into their household?"

"I will," said Hauka.

When they reached the pa Perere pretended not to be aware that his brother was a cripple. He didn't have to feign interest in Turongo's wood-carving; his astonishment was genuine. So was that of the visitors.

"Nobody in Lanai does work as fine as this!" Huloa cried. "Where do you get such ideas?"

"Some just seem to come into my mind," Turongo replied. "Others I copy from things I see. A kaka parrot suggested that face. A tuatara lizard gave me the expression for this one. The curved fronds of tree ferns suggested these scrolls."

It warmed Kura's heart to hear the praise of the

strangers. My Turongo is also great in his way, she thought happily.

Huge was the feast served to welcome the long-absent men and their friends from far-off lands; long were the speeches which followed. When the ceremonies were over Perere went to his mother. He found her looking up at the huge bunch of bananas which she had hung from a rafter to finish ripening.

"Fetch the plants ashore," she directed. "I want to put them out at once—" Her heart sank as she saw the expression on her son's face. "She didn't offer you some banana plants?"

"No—and I didn't think of asking for them," he confessed.

Kura tried to hide her disappointment. How true was that saying about seeking feathers on fish before expecting sense from a man or woman in love! Still, it would be nice to have even this one bunch of the fruit for which she never ceased to long. . . .

"I'll go back to get some plants as soon as I can," Perere promised.

Marama saw little of her betrothed for days. Only necessary work was being done. Every morning the men crowded into the meeting-house to listen to the next instalment of Perere's account of his travels, while the women stole up on the outside of the walls of raupo reeds and stood with ears pressed against them to hear what was being said. Not until the umu oven pits were opened for the evening meal did Perere cease talking.

Then all the men helped to overhaul Huloa's canoe or to prepare food for him to use on the trip. The stars which appeared in the eastern sky just before sunrise showed that the sailing season would soon be over, and the visitors were anxious to be off while they had the advantage of the south-west winds for the first part of the long journey back to Lanai.

They carried many gifts with them when they sailed. Each had a flax cloak. Turongo gave Huloa a carved feather-box. Two female kuri dogs, in pup, were put aboard. The lumps of pounamu stone were the greatest treasure of all. Huloa had been shown how it had to be sawn, and he said that the tools made from it would be handed down in his country as precious heirlooms.

He intended to make Tahiti his first calling-place, and the people in the next village had given him many messages to deliver to their friends and relatives. "Tell my brother I forgive him for driving me away," said their chief. "Thanks to him, I now have much land in this new country."

17

THE MANIANGA STRIKE AGAIN

A few weeks after the marriage of Perere and Hine-Marama a large log was floated down the river from the forest, and a group of workmen, under Perere's supervision, began to turn it into a seven-man canoe.

"As soon as it's ready I'll sail up the coast and get banana plants from Rona," Perere told his mother.

Kura gazed into the distance. What memories of her homeland had been stirred by eating that one bunch of golden-skinned fruit!

"Why not put this work towards the building of a great ocean-going canoe?" she inquired. "Or is that huge tree with the tapu sign on it to be still growing up there when I'm dead?"

"Such a task would occupy five times as many men for the best part of a year," he replied. "I've mentioned it to Ruapara. He say's he'd also like to see his Hawaiki again. But other things must come first."

Kura sighed as she heard it.

"But when I become high chief it'll be the first order I'll give," Perere assured her.

Kura tried to think hopefully of that day, but at the back of her mind was a vague fear. Something would prevent it from being done! Years ago they could have used the one belonging to those Tahitians, or built one like the *Tere-Moana*, if it hadn't been for their foes the Manianga. Now that same vindictive tribe might wreck the promise made by her son. . . .

Her fears were confirmed a few days later. Four scouts

who had been absent for a long time returned to the pa, and all the leading men were summoned to a conference. It was held in the new meeting-house, built to replace an old one which had grown too small for the tribe's increased population.

It was a very fine building, fifteen paces long by ten paces wide. Turongo, who now had four assistants to do the roughing out, was decorating it with carved barge-boards, doorposts, lintels, and wall panels.

Old Ruapara took his seat in the front row of the gathering, flanked by Perere, Hauka, Meiva, and a few lesser chiefs. Before them, haggard and tired from their arduous and dangerous journey, were the four scouts. Their leader made his report.

They had gone to the fringe of the country which the Manianga now occupied. On the pre-arranged day, when the star Atutahi made its first appearance for the year in the eastern sky at dawn, they had met Makatiti, their secret agent.

It was just as well that they had trained Makatiti so thoroughly for the part which he had to play! Several times the Manianga leaders had awakened him in the night to ask questions, hoping to catch him out if his story was false. But he had never faltered in his replies. Now the Manianga believed what he told them and had accepted him into the tribe. He had married one of their slave girls.

They consulted him on everything connected with their projected attack on the Tere-Moana tribe. He had convinced them that the route which he advised was the best one for their taua to take. It was the only way they could avoid crossing several ranges of steep hills.

Scouts had gone along this route through the valleys, and had returned to confirm what Makatiti had said. This time the Manianga were determined to leave nothing to chance. Day after day their fighting-men practised the laying of ambushes, hand-to-hand fighting, and night attacks. They also went for long training marches.

Nor had they forgotten how their original pa had been burned out by the throwing of burning sticks over the palisade. This had also been practised.

"They'll need some mighty throwers to reach any of our houses!" Ruapara commented. "None are nearer than eighty paces to our palisade!"

The scout leader went on to say that age hadn't mellowed the tempers of the old Manianga women. They kept the young men up to the mark by telling them that they must exact utu vengeance for the past defeats—and those deadly, unforgivable insults about the cloaks which they had made.

Unfortunately, Makatiti had no idea when the attack would be made. It might take place in autumn, after the kumara crop was harvested—and it could be deferred until the following spring. The final decision would rest with the Manianga chief.

When the report of the scouts ended and questions had been asked, Ruapara announced his decision. It upset the whole pattern of the tribal life and inflicted hardships on every one. Until winter brought a brief respite, a string of scouts would have to watch the route though the hills, with a relay of runners to carry news of a Manianga advance. Other men would have to carry food to those outposts. All young men not engaged on this work would have to undergo a rigorous training in fighting and marching.

Naturally all the garden work, the fishing, and hunting would fall on the older men, the women, boys, and girls. Nobody would have any leisure.

Kura went about with a set face after Perere brought her the news. Just when the tribe had seemed to be winning real prosperity, with time to spare for the arts of carving and weaving as well as sports and games, everything which made life pleasant had to be abandoned for defence work!

Even her Turongo had to lay aside his carving and turn his hand to the making of spears and clubs.... To think that a few vindictive Manianga widows were behind it all!

Just a part of this same effort would have built the ocean-going canoe which could have taken her, with Ruapara, Hauka, Ngaio, and other older people, on that longed-for visit to their Hawaiki! In a few more years it would be too late to think of it.

"What can we do?" Perere protested, when he had listened to her bitter comments. "None of us wants to slave like this. But we must be ready to meet the Manianga when they come." In a savage tone he added, "Perhaps nothing short of the extermination of our enemies will bring peace. I wish Maui had done it while he had the chance!"

The crops were dug and stored, every one remained on the alert, but no attack came. At great personal risk a scout made a winter journey through the fog-shrouded hills, managed to confer with Makatiti by a combination of luck and daring, and was told that the attack had been put off.

"On this side of Aotearoa the winds are colder and stronger than in our country," Makatiti explained. "They were worse than usual this year, and so the kumara crops were poor. There was no spare food for a taua to take with them. They may attack after the crops have been planted in the spring."

But when the warm weather returned the Manianga again put off the attack. By arrangement Makatiti met another lot of messengers on an appointed day. "All the omens were very unfavourable," he explained. "The Tohunga priests forbade the taua to start."

Another summer passed in unending vigilance, hard training for the fighting-men, and constant toil for every one else. Kura went one day to the river-bank, lifted off some of the thatching which protected the log which was to have been made into a canoe to fetch the banana plants, then replaced it again. For over a year not a stroke of work had been done on it!

Then came the autumn morning when an exhausted runner staggered into the pa and gasped, "They come!" While the fighting-men mustered on the marae, Ruapara and Perere questioned the messenger. The Manianga were coming by the route which Makatiti had advised them to take, they learned, and there would be just enough time for the Tere-Moana taua to get into position to ambush the enemy.

After the fighting-men had marched away Marama sat with her first-born in her arms, weeping softly. Kura tried to comfort her. "I know what it's like when your husband goes out to battle," she said, "but perhaps this'll be the last time we have to fight the Manianga. We should win. Perere is a great leader. All the omens are favourable, too."

"Why can't we go away to where I was born?" Marama suggested. "It's such a lovely island. Nobody could attack us there. Perere found only one spot where you can land— and he said it couldn't be used if the sea's rough. We could keep watch there on calm days."

Kura caught her breath sharply. This was something which had never occurred to her!

"After our men defeat the Manianga others might attack us," Marama pointed out. "My father says tribes living on the one island always fight. But if we built some canoes and went to my island we'd be safe."

It would solve all these troubles, Kura reflected. Marama had often described her island, where the tall pine-trees grew. It was much warmer than this country, with plenty of good soil for gardens. If they went there one of the canoes could sail on to her Hawaiki, returning with pigs, fowls, and young trees. She would go with it, of course. . . .

She hurried away to discuss it with Ngaio. Hauka was in the house, twisting up thread for a new fishing-line. He listened for a time to what the women were saying, then inquired, "And how many canoes should we have to build?"

Kura stared at him, all her hopes dashed. She might have known there would be something wrong with the idea. There were now many hundred people in the tribe. Even though the trip was a fairly short one, a canoe couldn't carry more than fifty people.... Yes, it was hopeless to think of it....

A day and night of forced marches, with only a few short periods of rest, brought the taua led by Perere to the valley with steep sides which had been selected as the site of the ambush. When his men had hidden themselves in the scrub and tall bracken on either side of the pass, Perere sent a few scouts off to travel by way of the hill-crests to signal the approach of the enemy.

Perere had a brief sleep, to awaken full of the desire for action. He could imagine the dismay of the Manianga when armed men sprang out of the ferns and charged down on both flanks of their column....

The day wore on. At first Perere welcomed the respite because it gave his men a chance to rest, but by midday he was becoming anxious. He sent a few more scouts off to see why the first lot hadn't signalled a warning of the enemy approach.

Rustlings in the bracken showed that most of the hidden men were now awake. Word was passed along to him, asking permission for a few at a time to go down to drink at the little stream which could be heard gurgling below. Every one was still very thirsty after that long march; all water-gourds were empty.

He forbade it. No matter how cautiously they crept down, they would leave tracks through the fern for

L

the Manianga men to see. Nothing must spoil this ambush! More time dragged by, and a sense of dire forebod-
ing began to grip Perere. This wasn't the only route
through the mountains! What if the enemy had changed
their plans at the last moment?

The sun sank lower in the western sky, and still there
was no signal from the watchers on the heights above.

They must come this way, Perere thought, trying to con-
vince himself. What were those fellows up on the hill-
crests doing? Had they all gone to sleep?

It was the longest day Perere had ever known, but the
sun set at last, the dusk came down, and he gave the order
to withdraw to the hill-tops, walk a short distance along
them, and descend into the valley again for the night. A
few men must stay behind to tell the returning scouts what
had been done. He waited until his taua had moved out,
then followed.

When he rejoined them some were drinking thirstily
from the creek, while others were opening their food
baskets and eating. He sat apart from the rest, full of
gloom. He tried to tell himself that the Manianga were
taking their time; they would be along in the morning.

One scout after another came in, to report having seen nothing moving. Soon only one scout was unaccounted for.

Perere made a round to see that all the sentries had been posted, then lay down, wrapped in his cloak. In spite of his worries, he started to doze, only to awaken with a start when he heard a sentry's challenge. Hurrying across, club in hand, he found the missing scout had returned. The man was very tired.

"I waited at my post for a time," he reported. "Then I saw a place ahead which looked as if it would command a wider view. I moved to it, keeping under cover of trees. When I reached it I saw an even better one farther on——"

"Never mind all these details," Perere interrupted. "What is your news?"

"Finally I crawled to the summit of a high hill and peered over the top. I could look down on many gullies. One runs down to the plain over there to the south——"

"Yes, yes," Perere prompted impatiently. "Did you see men moving down it?"

"No. You can't look into the bottom of it from where I was——but I did see birds flying up at intervals, always farther down than the last lot——"

"Where have you been since?" Perere said angrily.

"I started back, but darkness overtook me. I went into the wrong gully first——"

There was another challenge from a sentry, a reply, and a growing clamour of voices. Perere heard his name called. He hurried forward, pushed his way through a gathering crowd, and found a panting man being supported by two others. Peering into his face, Perere recognized one of the men who had been left on hill-tops overlooking the east coast, to keep a watch on the rear.

"Our pa . . . under attack," the man gasped. "Signal fire . . . was lit . . . some time ago. . . . I couldn't . . . get here quicker. . . ."

Perere listened to the growing clamour around him,

stunned by the news, yet aware that he had begun to expect something of the kind. He could tell by the sullen note in the voices around him that he had lost much of his mana by allowing himself to be outwitted like this. Then he pulled himself together.

"Silence!" he commanded. Those close to him obeyed, but farther off the growling criticisms were still audible. From out of the darkness somebody suggested that they start running for home.

"No!" Perere roared, then added, "What use would it be for a few at a time to arrive, exhausted by running? We shall march as a taua, resting when necessary. We must be fit to fight when we get there. Let every man collect his food-basket and fill his water-gourd!"

He went back for his own gear, walked down to put himself in the lead, then ordered all cloaks to be dropped. "At the pace I'll set you'll soon be warm enough without them!" He waited for the last order to be obeyed, then started off at a steady run. Behind him rose the drumming sound of nearly a hundred and fifty pairs of feet.

18

THE DEFENCE OF THE PALISADE

As the Maniangas made attack after attack on the palisade Kura began to abandon hope. Small parties of the enemy, coming up the river by swimming or in commandeered Tere-Moana fishing-canoes, kept clawing their way up the steep sides of the bluff, so many of the defenders had to patrol its crest, depleting the numbers of those who defended the high fence across the narrow neck of land where the fish-net battle had been fought years ago.

The old men had done most of the fighting at first, but now nearly all of them were dead. Ruapara had fallen while dealing with a sneak attack which came up the rugged path where Turongo had suffered his accident. Hauka had died defending a spot where a log battering-ram had weakened the palisade.

Meiva, still unwounded, had taken charge. Carrying the short stabbing-lance which he preferred to a club, he directed the women and the few remaining old men to threatened points. While his followers struck at those who were trying to break in, he stood back to deal with anyone who managed it. Several times he had run his lance through a howling warrior just as the man was about to strike down the defenders from behind.

Whenever there was a lull Kura went about inquiring if anyone had seen Turongo, or had found his body, for the cripple had been missing since the attack began. He had been seen last as he hobbled towards the path down the bluff. She at length concluded that he had died defending that spot and his body must have fallen into the river.

"We'll never see our Hawaiki again," said Ngaio, bringing Kura some eel-meat and a gourd of water. "We'll all die defending our homes." She spoke with difficulty, for a glancing blow from a club had bruised her face severely. "It's no use grieving. I'm only sorry for the children who'll be taken away to slavery."

"We aren't beaten yet," Kura said stoutly, although she too feared it was only a matter of time. She found herself hoping that little Marama would be killed instead of living to be a Manianga drudge.

Her three daughters, bloodstained and weary, came to sit by her as she kept watch. "How did the enemy outwit our Perere like this?" said the eldest.

"I can only suppose they knew all along that Makatiti was our spy," she said wearily. "They were able to fool us into thinking they'd come by the route he advised them to take; then they took another way."

Meiva came along, staring across the top of the palisade. "They're giving us a longer rest than usual this time," he remarked; then he assisted some women to strut and brace a weak spot. On the head of the bluff another signal fire blazed up, lit in case Perere's rearguard hadn't seen the first one.

The time went by, and still the attacks were not renewed, but in a patch of forest near by the defenders could hear adzes thudding and the occasional crash of a tree falling. The Manianga were evidently getting more logs ready to use for battering at the palisade.

The attack came just before dawn, and it was deadlier than any of the preceding ones. Groups of men charged forward, carrying logs whose ends they rammed into the stout fence. Rails and stakes began to break, and the palisade started to lean inward as posts were loosened in the earth.

This is the end, Kura thought; soon the Manianga will be able to run up the sloping fence and jump off the top, or they'll make a big gap and pour through it. Holding her club in both hands, she struck at the heads of those who tried to climb the sagging palisade.

Another log crashed against the fence close to where she stood and a gap appeared. With howls of triumph the dark figures of the attackers crowded towards it. Meiva ran his lance through the first man to enter, then killed the second one, only to be slain himself by a long spear thrust up from the ditch below.

Without knowing how she came to be there Kura found herself standing over Meiva's body, surrounded by other women who also fought with the fury of despair. They struck blindly at anything which showed in the gap. Behind them they heard an increasing clamour from the edge of the bluff.

The enemy had at last succeeded in gaining a footing at the head of the path, she supposed. Suddenly some young men pushed past her, armed with long spears, with which they jabbed down at the Manianga warriors in the ditch. Dazed and with her arms and shoulders aching, blood running down her face from a scalp wound which she didn't remember receiving, she looked along the defences.

More men were there, shouting insults at the Maniangas and thrusting at them with spears.

She staggered back. What did it mean? Who were these men? The clamour of the fighting died, and the attackers retreated. The newcomers began to heave the palisade back into place and block the gap with anything they could find. In the first light of dawn Kura recognized some of Turongo's beautifully carved slabs being used as struts.

Somebody tugged at her arm, and she turned to see Ngaio, who gasped, "Those Tahitians were only just in time! They've now repaid anything they owed us!"

"The Tahitians?" Kura repeated blankly, staring at the line of men working in frantic haste to repair the fence. "How did they get here?"

"In canoes. They came up the river. We wouldn't believe they were friends when they started to climb the path. We thought it was a Manianga trick. But Turongo shouted to us, and we recognized his voice——"

"Turongo?" Kura cried. "Then he wasn't killed——"

"No. He's asking for you. Come along."

Ngaio led her to where Turongo sat, leaning against a tree. The little crowd around the cripple made way for her. He smiled up at her.

"There are more ways of fighting than using a club or spear," he said triumphantly. "I can't run, and my walk is only a shuffle—but no man can paddle better than I!

"When the attack began I knew there was only one thing for me to do. I crawled down the path to my little canoe. Already I could see Manianga warriors getting into our fishing-canoes or swimming towards me. I saw they intended to try to enter our defences from the rear. I shouted a warning to those above, then pushed off in my canoe." He paused to drink from the gourd of water which one of his sisters had brought.

"I paddled away, dodging the canoes which tried to

block the way and striking at the heads of those swimmers who tried to upset me. I broke through."

"You're a true son of your brave, clever father," Kura cried.

"Outside the bay the big waves threatened to swamp my little canoe. I had to bail it out often. But I paddled towards the village of our friends the Tahitians. I reached it at last. They sent off a runner to summon the Motu, then every one of their fighting-men jumped into their big fishing-canoes. I helped to paddle all the way back." He took another drink from the gourd.

"You know the rest," he said, his voice suddenly weak.

Kura turned to the crowd of women and children. "The men who came to our aid must be fed!" she ordered. "See to it!" She returned to the palisade. "Food will be brought soon," she told the leader of the Tahitians.

"We can do with it," he replied. "Never have men paddled harder than we did coming here!" He stared over the top of the palisade. In the growing light he could see the Manianga a couple of hundred paces away, grouped around food-baskets. "They'll attack again as soon as they've eaten and rested," he said. He looked down at the bodies sprawled in the ditch below.

"The fight you women made will live in our legends," he said admiringly.

"Nearly all our old men have died in defence of the pa," she pointed out. "Our high chief, Ruapara, was among them. So was Meiva and my friend Hauka."

The eastern sky flushed red, a golden glow replaced it, and then the sun came up. The Manianga gathered in a group and the voice of a chief could be heard addressing them. Suddenly a stir and bustle began among the enemy. They could be seen running to gather their gear.

The pa defences were manned, but the Manianga did not advance. Kura saw the enemy picking up baskets and cloaks. A murmur of astonishment broke from the

Tere-Moana people as they saw the Manianga hurry away, heading for the fern and scrub country to the south.

"Our taua returns!" screamed a boy who had climbed a tree, pointing to a cloud of dust on the plain to the westward. With sighs of relief the weary defenders relaxed. A prayer of thankfulness rose in Kura's heart; then she remembered that work still had to be done.

"Food must be ready for our men when they arrive!" she directed. "Fill every water-gourd!" She went in search of Marama and found her building a fire in an umu oven pit. "Perere's baby is safe?" she inquired anxiously.

"Yes." Marama pointed to a basket. "He sleeps there. If the Manianga had overwhelmed us, and I was still alive, I intended to slide down the cliff on a rope I had ready, taking him with me, and swim across the river. Then I would have tried to make my way to the Motu pa."

"You know your father is dead?" Kura said gently.

"Yes. My mother too. She was killed beside me."

Kura walked to where she could see the cloud of dust raised by the feet of the returning taua. By the way in which it was moving she knew that the men in it were running. She looked around for a messenger and called to an active boy.

"Run out and tell Perere there is no need for haste," she directed. "The enemy has fled."

When the taua marched in the weary men dropped to the ground. The women gathered around them, serving them with food and water. Perere, the sweat drying in streaks on his dust-covered body, ate standing. Between mouthfuls he talked to the leader of the Tahitians.

"We must pursue them," Perere said after a time. Groans and cries of protest rose from his men. They couldn't do it after running all night! He pointed out that the Manianga would also be weary, and should be easy to overtake, but it had little effect.

This showed how he had lost mana, Perere thought

bitterly. He said a few words to Marama, looked into the basket where his little son lay sleeping, then came back and spoke to his men. "I'm going. If any wish to follow they can." He took his lance and club, then walked towards the gate in the palisade without looking back.

The leader of the Tahitians and a few of his men followed. Presently some Tere-Moana men struggled to their feet and set off. Eventually Perere found himself at the head of nearly fifty warriors, some of whom were the first of the Motu to arrive at the pa.

They overtook many stragglers before the main body of the Manianga escaped into the hills. From a mortally wounded man Perere learned how the enemy had been able to outwit him.

Makatiti was too fond of the slave woman whom he had married to abandon her. Before he marched with the Manianga taua he revealed his identity to her, and told her to make for a spot in the hills, where he would meet her after the battle and take her to his people.

But she had been unwilling to leave her sister in captivity. Unknown to Makatiti, she arranged for this woman to accompany her. The sister had a lover among the Manianga fighting-men, and she warned him of the ambush, hoping he would escape the impending massacre. He went straight to the chief and revealed the plot.

"We killed Makatiti and the two women," said the dying man, "then we took a different route through the mountains." He showed his teeth in a grin of savage regret. "But for the arrival of those Tahitians we would have beaten you at last! We were going to slay every one in your pa, then ambush you as you returned!"

With a last effort the man added, "Then the old women of my tribe would have had to find something else to complain about!"

So one young woman defeated all my plans, thought Perere, as he gave orders for the pursuit to be abandoned.

When the dead had been buried, the tangi mourning ceremonies were over, and the mess was cleaned up, Kura realized that her last chance of seeing her Hawaiki again had gone. Perere was now the high chief, but it would take him years to regain the mana which he had lost.

He couldn't order an ocean-going canoe to be built. There had been quite a lot of grumbling and protest when he had instructed some workmen to finish making that seven-man craft to enable banana plants to be procured from Wahine-Rona-Nui.

As disheartening as anything was the fact that the fighting had been inconclusive. Neither side could claim a victory. Most of the Manianga warriors had escaped, and they still had to obtain utu vengeance for their previous defeats. As a result her people would have to go on standing ready to repel another attack.

This meant that the young men must continue their training, while the older people did most of the work.

She discussed the problems with Ngaio when they were weaving winter clothing for their grandchildren. "It all comes back to the fact that men can't live at peace with each other," her old friend remarked.

"Always thirsting for utu," Ngaio went on. "There's always some grudge or other. Now some of our young men want to take the initiative by raiding the Manianga! If I had a voice in the councils I'd forbid it! This last lot of fighting took the lives of Hauka, my husband, and Maka-titi, my son!"

"If we send a taua against the Manianga, Perere will lead it—and, as happened with his father, Maui, he mightn't come back," said Kura. "But it's no good holding the men responsible for everything. We're just as much to blame."

"I don't see that, Kura!"

"Well, your son was killed because a woman betrayed

our plans. And don't forget how a few spiteful old Mani-anga women are at the bottom of it all."

"And why are they so vindictive towards us? Because one of our men made an insulting comment on the work they'd put into those cloaks! You know as well as I do that it was quite unfair. They were very well made indeed!"

Kura gave up trying to reason with her friend. Ngaio had become very bitter and sharp-tongued since the loss of her husband and one of her sons.

19

THE LAMENT OF HINE-MOANA

"It's a bit cold for her to be out of doors," one of the grey-haired women suggested.

"There's no cloud, and it's warm when you're out of the wind," said the other. "Seems to be the first real feel of spring in the air, too. Even if she has to be brought inside again soon it'll do her good to have a bit of sunshine. As long as she's left to crouch over a fire she does nothing but brood."

At a sign from one of the two surviving daughters a couple of stalwart young Maori men stepped forward to help the aged Kura to her feet. A daughter put the walking-staff in her hand, and the men took her to the door, ready to support her if she stumbled.

The old woman halted and blinked when she felt the sun on her face, then shuffled forward again. The men helped her to the sheltered nook among the boulders on the summit of the bluff, overlooking the river-mouth and the bay. After aiding her to lower herself into a sitting position one of the daughters tucked the warm dogskin cloak around her mother. Kura relaxed against the rock which served as a back-rest.

It was good to feel the sun on your face and hands again, she thought. Better than a fire. . . . She closed her eyes for a time, to open them when Perere, now stout, grey-bearded, but still active, came to pay his respects.

"My banana plants?" she inquired.

"We're looking after them," he assured her. "They'll

bear fruit again this summer. The first flower-stalk's grow-ing now."

Kura smiled. Eating the fruit which was tapu to every one else was the one pleasure now left in her life. A frown crept over her face. "Marama hasn't been to see me lately," she complained.

Perere did not reply. It must be one of his old mother's bad days, otherwise she would remember that her beauti-ful daughter-in-law had been dead for years.

His face wore a wistful expression as he thought of Marama. Now his clearest memory of her was as he had seen her first; a wild, shy girl standing in a creek on the island where she was born. The Moon Maiden.... Never had a woman been better named! Even when she had be-come a grandmother she was still famous for her beauty....

"The Manianga! Is a look-out being kept for them?" Kura said sharply.

"They'll never attack us again," he told her. He did not remind her that the Tere-Moana, allied with four other exasperated tribes, had descended on those incorrigible trouble-makers long ago, killing off most of the fighting-men and carrying the survivors, with all their women and children off to slavery.

When Kura closed her eyes and dozed, Perere walked away, pausing to tell some playing children to keep a watch on the old woman. In the respectful tone proper for addressing a famous chief they promised to do it.

In her dreams Kura drifted into the past. She saw her-self sitting by a fire with Ngaio and an old man; sole sur-vivors of those who had manned the canoe which brought them to this new land. Outside the house a bitter south-west wind was blowing, rattling squalls of rain and bursts of hail on the thatch overhead.

As usual, their thoughts had turned to the homeland which lay far beyond the horizon's rim, the birthplace which they had never seen again. They recalled the days when the blood of youth ran strongly in bodies now stiff and aged.

"Our Hawaiki was a lovely place," Ngaio sighed.

They talked of its warm nights, the rich fruits, a sea never too cold for swimming. Going out at dawn to lure the octopus from its reef crannies. . . . The excitement of finding a good catch in a fish-trap. . . . Those dances on the stone-paved marae on moonlit nights, when your feet seemed to move of their own accord in time to the throbbing of the sharkskin drums. . . .

"Strange how those born here have no urge to see our ancestral home," the old man observed.

"I would have loved to see my family and friends again," Kura had said. She still thought of those whom she had left as being unchanged from when she had seen them last. It did not seem possible that they too had grown old or were now dead.

After a time Kura awakened, to see one of her great-grandchildren sitting by her feet and making a garland of rata blossoms. She gave the little one an indulgent smile. Presently the string of flowers was handed to her for inspection.

Kura ran them through her wrinkled claws of hands. They were pretty, but not to be compared with those lovely tiare flowers which she had strung for her own head and neck so long ago. She let the child take them from her and stared into vacancy, her expression one of surprise.

Why had she been thinking of all those things as happening at some far-off time? It now seemed as if it was only yesterday when she was a child like the one at her feet. . . . How clear were the memories of her girlhood to-day.

The child ran back to her playmates, and Kura dozed again. The wind dropped, and it became hot in the nook among the sun-warmed rocks. The old woman dreamed that she was again in the big canoe during the blazing heat of that long and dreadful calm. Her puckered mouth mumbled, and her hands twitched. Suddenly she opened her eyes.

"I paddled as long as any of the men, then I steered," she said proudly. She blinked and looked around, wondering to whom she had been talking. I must have dreamed, she decided.

What a fine, brave man was her husband, Maui! How proud he had been when she nursed her first-born! And she herself had done her best to live up to the traditions of the Rangatira. . . .

Her thoughts roved to that desperate defence of the pa against the Manianga. Although her younger son was a cripple, he had saved the day. Why didn't Turongo take her to admire his latest carving? A feeling of desolation chilled her when she remembered that he was now dead.

She stared in the direction in which her birthplace lay, and it seemed as though she could again feel the *Tere-Moana* canoe rolling and pitching on the ocean swells.

M

Then she was back in the present once more, with tears dimming her sight as she remembered that she was now the only one of the crew left alive. She began to croon that ancient lament of her people, the Tangi of Hine-Moana, Maid of the Ocean, whose sad voice is heard ever in the ceaseless wash of the restless sea.

As if in answer to her song of mourning for those now dead and the Hawaiki which she would never see again, the cries and laughter of the children on their near-by playground seemed to change to voices calling from a spot far away, while the scrub upon the distant headland took on the appearance of coconut palms, silhouetted against the milk-white sky of a tropical dawn. The dull boom and rumble of surf on a coral reef rang in her ears once more.

Scenes from her childhood flitted through her mind. Being shown how to string flowers . . . her mother guiding her fingers as she plaited her first mat . . . lessons in the beating of tapa cloth. How musically the little wooden mallets had rung as the sheets of bark were hammered thin!

Then she was again making a fine mat, one which the older women would admire. What an important period in the history of her people had begun when she had sighted the sail of Rehua's little canoe! That brute of a Pararaka had wanted to kill him. . . .

Rehua had been a gallant old chief. How bravely he had walked out to face the Manianga taua, sacrificing his life to gain time for his people to prepare their defence. . . .

Me mate te tangata me mate mo te whenua: To die in defence of your land was the death of a warrior. . . .

It had been her idea to trap enemies with a fishing-net. She had suggested it first to Maui when he was engaged in a sham fight on their island home; she had reminded him of it on that day when they awaited the Manianga attack. Maui had received all the credit on both occasions.

But that was only right and proper. It was a woman's place to stand behind her man, content to let such things increase his mana and happy in the knowledge that in his heart he would appreciate the aid and advice.

Her heart swelled with pride as she thought of how she had tried to act in that way all her life. Giving wise guidance to the men. . . . Not like those vicious old harridans of the Manianga, who had sent so many young men to their deaths—merely to gratify their wounded vanity!

Again she seemed to feel the pitching of the great canoe as the wind in its bellying brown sail drove it down the Ara-Moana towards this new land. Tears misted her sight once more, yet through them, as one sees objects when heavy rain is falling, she saw her Hawaiki. This time it was real; she had been able to go home after all!

Garlanded with flowers, arms outstretched in welcome, all her people were hurrying towards her. Above them long leaf-plumes of the coconut palms thrashed and rattled in the wind. Piled white clouds sailed steadily across the sky. Loud and clear sounded the surf on the reef. Her people had halted and were beckoning. With a glad cry she ran towards them. . . .

Her walking-staff clattered on the rocks as it fell. The children stopped playing to stare, then they stole forward, wide-eyed. Suddenly a girl screamed.

Men and women ran from the houses, to halt at the sight of that figure among the rocks, as motionless as if carved from grey-brown stone and with the face turned towards the north-east. One of the daughters stole forward and touched Kura with a trembling hand. The staring eyes did not flicker.

Softly at first, then gaining strength and poignancy, the heart-stirring tangi cries arose from the women. The men stood with heads bent. Tears ran down Perere's beard.

Kura had journeyed Ki te Po te Hokia ki Taiao; to the world beyond, from which none return. Her spirit had flown to Te Reinga, there to pass into the care of Hine-Nui-te-Po; the Great Lady of the Night.

When the body had been carried away, surrounded by wailing women, Perere looked at the awed, silent group of children, standing among their scattered toys. He motioned them to sit before him.

"This is a very sad day," he said huskily. "The last living tie with our Hawaiki has broken."

"She spoke to me a short time ago," sobbed a girl. "She said my flowers were strung nicely."

"That'll be something to tell your children in days to come," said Perere.

He glanced in turn at the many boys and girls who were related to the dead woman. "You'll be proud to claim descent from Maui and Kura when you grow up. Such an ancestry places you among the high-born Rangatira. It also carries obligations. Whenever there is doubt in your mind ask yourself what Maui or Kura would have done." He gazed across the reed-fringed river and the flax swamps to the distant hills which marked the boundary of the tribal lands.

"There is your country. You can retain it only by loyalty to our tribe. It isn't enough to keep fires burning on your land. You must be ready to fight in defence of your heritage."

He looked at a small fenced plot on a low rise, then to a long strip on the river-bank, enclosed with carved posts and rails of totara wood.

"Guard any tapu ground. The spot over there is hallowed because Rehua, the great canoe chief, died on it. Down here the *Tere-Moana* canoe lies buried. When you boys grow up you will be told of the secret places where the bones of your ancestors were laid to rest."

He looked at the solemn, respectful children. They were too young to understand now—but they might remember his words and realize their full meaning when they were

older. He was turning away, when a little girl handed him
a garland of rata flowers.

"They'll be placed around Kura's neck," he told her.
"She'll know they came from you." He walked towards the
little hut where the body was being laid out.

EPILOGUE

On the bank of a river in the North Island of New Zealand is a piece of ground surrounded by a fence of carved posts and rails. Whenever they decay new ones are erected in their place.

No Maori sets foot within this enclosure, for a tapu guards the spot where a great canoe was buried seven hundred years ago.

At the head of this strip of ground, set in a massive plinth of concrete to foil future attempts to steal it, is the big anchor stone which this canoe carried down the long Ara-Moana sea-path from a Hawaiki far away. Now it serves as the headstone at the grave of the ship in Aotearoa, Land of Long, Bright Days.

Living in this district are many Maori of Rangatira rank. When referring to their ancestors they say proudly, "We are descended from Maui and Kura."

ABOUT THIS BOOK

PRONUNCIATION GUIDE

Failure to give the correct pronunciation to the proper names and Polynesian phrases in this book will rob it of an essential feature.

The rules are simple and easy to grasp. There are no silent vowels. Each should be used as a syllable. Where two or more vowels come together each is pronounced separately and given equal emphasis. Sound *a* as in *father*, *e* as in *eh* or *whey*, *i* as in *police*, *o* as the *aw* in *raw*, *u* as in *Luke*.

The consonants are pronounced as in English. The *ng* sound is always pronounced as in the word *singer*, not as in *finger*. (Should you doubt the difference try to transpose *f* and *s* in these two words.) *Ng* at the beginning of a word is almost unknown in English. A simple expedient enables it to be pronounced correctly. Begin by saying *Singaio*. Then drop the *S* and say *Ingaio*. Now omit the *I* and give a slightly nasal intonation to *Ngaio*.

The following examples may help with the pronunciation, although a student of phonetics might call them barbarous:

Maui	...	...	...	*Mah-oo-ee*
Hikurangi	...	...	...	*He-koo-rahng-ee*
Kupe	...	...	...	*Coo-peh*
Aotearoa	...	...	...	*Ah-aw-tay-ah-raw-ah*
Maori	...	...	...	*Mah-aw-ree*
Taua	...	...	...	*Tah-oo-ah*
Manianga	...	...	...	*Mah-nee-ahng-ah*
Tere-Moana		...	...	*Tay-reh Maw-ah-nah*

THE BACKGROUND OF THIS BOOK

In their earlier book, *The First Walkabout*, the authors pictured Australia as it was between 10,000 and 15,000 years ago, when Negritos, the first human beings to inhabit the continent, entered a land very different from what it is to-day.

Once the necessary research work had been carried out, that task was comparatively easy. Geological evidence showed that at this period so much water had been locked up in the vast glaciers of the last phase of the Ice Age, which covered about one-third of the land surfaces of the world, that the ocean levels were some 250 feet lower than they are to-day. This laid bare an almost continuous bridge of land from South-east Asia to Tasmania. The few ocean channels which remained were narrow enough to be crossed with ease on crude rafts. Thus the diminutive Negrito folk were able to travel on foot over nearly the whole distance of their long migration, from tropical jungles in Malaya to the plains of Australia and eventually to what was then a sub-Antarctic climate in Tasmania.

Food remains on Negrito camp sites on the Australian mainland show that these people hunted animals now extinct, such as the giant diprotodon. Remains of vegetation indicate what the flora was like at the time, while other evidence shows a much cooler and wetter climate than that of to-day.

The writing of *The First Walkabout* was also aided by a study of Negrito people still living to-day, including a group surviving on the Australian mainland.

But in gathering the background material for *Rangatira* and reconstructing a chapter of prehistory the authors met far bigger problems. Archæological evidence on Pacific islands is mostly scanty, for the Polynesian people have always observed cleanliness in and around their dwelling sites, with most of the rubbish dumped into the sea or burnt. While commendable as regards sanitation and in the æsthetic sense, it means a dearth of those mounds of bones, ashes, discarded implements, worn-out clothing, lost or broken ornaments, and other occupational debris which prove such treasure-grounds for those who are piecing together the long story of man's sojourn on the earth and the growth of his cultures.

Only on camp sites in the South Island of New Zealand, dating to the very early Moa-hunter period of the Maori, as well as the Central Pacific island of Saipan and to a certain extent in Hawai'i, have any informative masses of evidence been found in the way of burials, food remains, personal adornments, and implements.

In spite of these difficulties, however, sufficient data have now been gathered to enable a reasonably clear picture to emerge of the Polynesians as they were during the period of the last of those great migrations, made in large sailing-canoes, which took these people to every habitable island in the Pacific and also to the shores of the surrounding continents.

Further, since the growth and spread of culture have tended to follow a similar pattern all over the world, what has been discovered concerning other peoples aids in interpreting evidence concerning the Polynesians.

One particularly significant piece of evidence in regard to the above is the way in which many people in the past have experienced an upsurge of energy, progress, and enterprise. The Greeks between 600 and 300 B.C. provide the most striking example, but there are numerous other parallels, some quite recent.

There is some evidence that the Polynesians may have gone through such a Golden Age period. Radio-carbon dating shows that the advance-guard of these people entered the Pacific much earlier than had been supposed. They were on Saipan at least 3100 years ago. There followed several periods of exploration and colonization, the last of which appears to have begun in the ninth century of the Christian era and ended in the fourteenth.

During this last period they were the greatest pioneer seafarers the world has known. Long before Columbus ventured across the Atlantic, Polynesians were making far more protracted voyages in canoes large enough to carry as many as fifty men and women, with stores for the voyage, domestic livestock in the form of pigs, fowls, and dogs, as well as seeds or rooted cuttings of their cultivated plants.

But when all the islands had been colonized the need for long voyages was over. Except in New Zealand, the Polynesians settled down to a more or less static way of life. Much of their knowledge of navigation was preserved in legends, but, as was inevitable among a people who had no written records, some was lost, as there was no longer any need for its practical application. In New Zealand they had what was to them a whole new world to explore and settle, so their sea voyaging was confined mainly to coastal waters.

Rangatira deals with the Polynesians when they were still full of prowess as seamen, at a period corresponding to the era in Europe prior to the battle of Crécy (1346).

Europe has seen vast changes since that day. They also occurred, though on a far smaller scale, in other parts of the world, including the Pacific. This will explain the difference between the authors' picture of the Polynesian colonists of 700 years ago and the Maori people as they were when Europeans contacted them first.

To mention only one point; there is no evidence that

the early arrivals in New Zealand were cannibals. Further, some inferences drawn by the authors from recent discoveries in cultural and physical anthropology are here published for the first time.

The authors thank the Board and Director of the South Australian Museum for opportunities to study such priceless material as the tapa-cloth specimens collected by Captain James Cook during his Pacific voyages and the original water-colours by George French Angas, illustrating Maori life prior to 1850. To the South Australian Branch of the Royal Geographical Society of Australasia they are deeply indebted for ready access to rare books and other data on early contacts between Europeans and the people of Polynesia.

NOTES

AOTEAROA, *derivation of.* This has proved to be a problem word to students of the Maori dialect of the Polynesian language, for it is capable of several translations, none of them adequate. One trouble is that *Ao* has several meanings. Just as the word "fast" in English can mean "speedy," "tied up," or "starvation," so does *Ao* mean "daytime," "world," or "cloud," with the context of the sentence usually giving the guide as to the sense in which it is used. But here we have no such aid; merely a noun followed by two adjectives, the first meaning "white" or "bright" and the second "long" or "lengthy." Thus it can be translated as "Long white cloud" or "Long bright world." The authors, however, favour a third alternative, "Land of Long, Bright Days." The reason for their choice lies in the fact that the Polynesian explorers, coming from the tropics, where the length of the day and night are almost equal throughout the year, would be bound to be impressed by the length of the days in the new land, for they visited it first when the midsummer days are longest.

ASTRONOMY. The Polynesians had a sound practical knowledge of the rudiments of this science. More than sixty bright stars were known to them by name. They also knew which stars would appear to pass directly over different islands at certain times of the year. This enabled navigators to set a course for a far-off destination by using some particular star as a guide. They knew nothing of the magnetic compass, but they had names for sixteen cardinal compass points. Their very accurate calendar was based upon the annual heliacal risings of certain bright stars or constellations, such as the Pleiades (Seven Sisters). From this calendar they knew the times of the year when favourable trade winds would be encountered on some particular voyage.

BANANAS, growing in New Zealand. Readers acquainted with the climate of the North Island as it is to-day may query the possibility of the first Polynesian colonists getting banana plants to grow there, even if well sheltered; but at the time with which this story deals, *circa* A.D. 1200, the earth was passing through a warm climatic phase, when grapes ripened out of doors in Southern England and the Danes established a colony in Greenland, whose people grazed cattle there. Botanical evidence, in the form of the growth rings of a huge King William pine at least a thousand years old, felled in Tasmania, shows that this warm phase also extended to the Southern Hemisphere. The authors have taken this into account in the story. The earth's climate became cooler again at around A.D. 1400, but there is evidence that we are now entering another warmer phase.

BIRDS AS LAND GUIDES. All pioneer seafarers found birds to be indispensable aids to navigation. The "Shore-sighting bird" of the Vikings was the shag, while the Phœnicians used the pigeon and the dove. They were carried in cages, and a bird was released when land was thought to be near. It would circle high into the sky. If it sighted land from its lofty elevation it would fly towards it, thus indicating the direction in which the ship should be steered. If no land was in sight it would return to the only resting-place available, the ship, which would sail on until a bird did sight land. The story of the dove in the Ark of Noah is a perfect example of the use of a shore-sighting bird. The Polynesians had no need to carry birds, for in their case the service was performed by the booby, tern, and frigate-bird. At the first light of dawn these birds leave their island homes and fly to feeding-grounds as far as fifty miles off shore, returning late in the afternoon. The captain of a Polynesian sailing-canoe, therefore, did not have to locate a speck of land lying isolated in a waste of sea, but a circle of ocean a hundred miles in diameter. Once he entered it the outward or homeward flights of the birds would soon show him where the land lay, thus greatly minimizing the danger of missing his objective. Lands lying thousands of miles away were located by captains following the direction taken by migrating bird flocks. The shining cuckoo led Kupe to New

Zealand, while the golden plover, which migrates from Alaska
to the Central Pacific each year, guided other explorers to the
Hawaiian Islands and thence to those lying off the coast of
British Columbia.

BREADFRUIT. Most people who have not visited the tropics
imagine breadfruit to be as described in that mine of misin-
formation, R. M. Ballantyne's *Coral Island*. This author seems
to have amplified the ambiguous description given in Captain
Cook's *Voyages*. If it is baked when full-sized but not yet ripe,
anyone with a strong imagination might describe its texture as
bearing some resemblance to bread, but actually it is more like
a mealy potato. If baked when ripe it resembles mashed sweet
potato to which condensed milk has been added. The Pacific
natives used to guard against food shortages by storing the ripe
fruit in leaf-lined pits, where it fermented and became something like cheese. This is still being done in a few islands.
When required a quantity is taken from the pit, wrapped in
leaves, baked, then pounded up and mixed with water to
form a paste (poi-poi) which resembles a stiff, tart-flavoured
custard.

The tree on which it grows is one of the most beautiful in
the Pacific. It will reach a height of from fifty to sixty feet, but
is usually pruned into a spreading shape to make it easier to
gather the fruit. The leaves are dark green, tough, and up to
three feet long, with bluntly serrated edges. Male and female
flowers are carried on the same tree, the former being like long
catkins, while the separate female ones are rounded receptacles
which form into the fruit. One variety, the jak, attains a weight
of over twenty pounds.

The tree is a native of Indonesia, and the Polynesians took it
with them to every Pacific island on which it would grow. The
seedless, cultivated form of it can be propagated only by root
cuttings. This fact supports the idea that the Polynesians came
to the Pacific via Indonesia and were not, as Thor Heyerdahl
claims, of North American origin. It also encourages the idea
that most of the earliest Polynesian journeys were made as
described in the first part of this book; by short stages, with
temporary settlements on small islands *en route*, for the life of
unplanted breadfruit cuttings is not overlong, and individual

trees have to grow to maturity before they can provide cuttings for propagation elsewhere.

CANOE VOYAGES. The Polynesians were the greatest pioneer seafarers the world has known. Their feats far outclass anything done by Phœnicians, Greeks, Norsemen, or Arabs. At least two thousand years before Columbus ventured across the Atlantic these people had made deep-water voyages more than twice as long. To refer to their ships as canoes is liable to create a false impression. Though of the canoe type, the craft were very seaworthy and up to a hundred feet in length. Captain Cook and his shipwrights were amazed at the sound workmanship that went into their construction, although the Polynesians had only stone tools with which to fell big trees, hollow them out to form the lower portions of the hulls, and to hew the boards used as topside planking. Running under sail before the trade wind, these craft covered about a hundred miles per day, which gives an average speed of over four knots.

CHARTS (page 121). Forty-three of these frameworks of thin sticks lashed together are preserved in the world's museums. While their main purpose was to aid the memory of the navigator, and they were not a map as we understand the term, they did serve a most useful purpose.

CHILDREN LEFT BEHIND BY MIGRANTS (page 46). This is by no means as heartless as it seems. One of the most likeable traits of Polynesian character is the fact that no such thing as a homeless child is found among them. If a youngster loses its parents it is at once adopted by some other household and there treated as one of the family. No matter how poor a Polynesian household may be, or how hard the people have to work in order to gain a living on some of the low atolls, there is always room and food in a home for an extra child, irrespective of its parentage.

CULTURE, diffusion of. There are two schools of thought concerning human progress through the various culture phases which culminate in civilization. One side maintains that simple, fundamental things such as the wheel, the plough, the baked clay pot, the bow and arrow, are such obvious ideas that they must have been discovered independently in many places, tending to appear in a community through sheer necessity.

This is known as the 'independent-invention' theory. The opposite view is taken by those who support the 'culture-diffusion' idea. They maintain that nearly all the basic inventions and discoveries tend to appear but once, and the idea then spreads to other peoples by diffusion through contact. In both cases the extreme ideas are equally untenable, for discoveries and inventions are made independently at times, but it is equally true that some discoveries, once thought to be the result of independent invention, have been proved by a further access of knowledge to provide yet another example of diffusion. One of the centres of invention and discovery during the rise of the practice of agriculture was around the Persian Gulf, the southern part of the Caspian Sea, and the Caucasus Mountains—an area sometimes called the "Cradle of Civilization." From there many ideas spread by diffusion. As archæologists dig up the sites of ancient cities and villages in this region the additional evidence thus gained tends to favour 'cultural diffusion' far more often than 'independent invention,' some of the links discovered lately being most convincing. In this book there are examples of both sides. Diffusion is illustrated when the Tere-Moana women see how the Manianga cloaks were made. Maui gaining useful information from the Motu tribe, and Perere learning a great deal from Huloa. Independent invention is shown by Turongo's original designs in his wood-carving. To-day we rely mainly upon books, newspapers, and technical journals to disseminate new knowledge, with the radio playing a very minor yet useful rôle, but the best results are still achieved in the original way, with people meeting at conferences, to exchange ideas and to have their minds stimulated by contact with others.

HAWAIKI. As is the case with Aotearoa, this word cannot be translated in a way which conveys its full meaning. As they colonized one group of islands after another the Polynesians bestowed this name, or dialectal variants of it such as Hawai'i and Savai'i, upon the place which they had left as well as upon the new homeland, just as we did when we named New South Wales, New England, New Plymouth, etc. Yet "Homeland" is not an adequate translation, for the word Hawaiki also holds a meaning akin to the "Dream Home" or "Dreamtime" of the

N

Australian aborigines, which is to them a vague, inherited memory of some other place in which their forefathers lived at one time.

HULOA'S CANOE, timber used in (page 121). The Polynesians of Hawai'i did not build their big ocean-going canoes of local wood, but used the trunks of giant Douglas fir-trees (Oregon pine) which they found floating at sea. These logs had drifted down from the north-west coast of America after floods in rivers had brought them to the ocean.

IO as supreme being in Maori pantheon. When Europeans first studied the religious beliefs of the Maori Io was mentioned only by the Tohunga priests among themselves. But a comparative study of the world's religions, especially those of the past, shows that most begin with a belief in some kind of mother goddess. In time she is given a father god as a companion. Then lesser gods and goddesses are introduced, usually as the offspring of the parent pair. Finally the original pair become background characters, mentioned by some type of priestly caste alone. But, as this story is laid at some time before the fourteenth century of the Christian era, the authors are of the opinion that the people as a whole would then be in that stage of a developing religion where the supreme being of their pantheon was still mentioned under special circumstances.

KON TIKI. Thor Heyerdahl, a Norwegian anthropologist, formed the theory that the Polynesians came originally from America. To prove that a drift voyage from South America to the Central Pacific was possible he and some companions built a raft of balsa wood, christened it *Kon Tiki*, and set out to drift with wind and current to Central Polynesia. They duly reached their objective, and Heyerdahl wrote a most entertaining and informative book about the plucky venture. Following this he published another book, of some 800 pages, *American Indians in the Pacific*, in which he set out everything in favour of his ideas. He failed, however, to account for some vitally important things—and hard facts can demolish the finest theory ever propounded. (*See also* Polynesians, origin of.)

KUPE. The account given in this book of the discovery of New Zealand by Kupe, at some time around A.D. 950, is an abridged version of the legend of the voyage which his people have handed down from generation to generation for a thousand years. Another legend of a notable voyage describes how Ui-te-Rangiora voyaged so far south that he sighted icebergs. The late Sir Peter Buck regarded the descriptions of floating ice as something added to the story after Polynesians had come into contact with Europeans, thus learning more about geography. He considered that the great cold would have made the lightly clad Polynesians turn back before they could have sailed to where ice can be seen. But the description of icebergs does not sound like a modern addition to the story. Further, east of the Chatham Islands, in the same latitude as Wellington, capital of New Zealand, is an area of ocean where floating ice is often sighted to-day, much farther north that it drifts elsewhere in the world. It is not in the least unlikely, therefore, that Ui-te-Rangiora did see "Islands of white rock floating on the sea."

Although not mentioned in legends, Polynesians must have voyaged to the Philippines, Formosa, and the coast around Hongkong, for their distinctive stone implements have been found there. This is also the case with the eastern and southern coasts of Australia. Another long voyage may have been made to the coast of Peru, to bring back not only the sweet potato native to that country, but its original name of 'kumara' as well. Traces of Polynesian influence seem to appear in stone implements found on the coasts of California and British Columbia.

KURI DOG. The Maori dog was small and not remarkable for its intelligence. It was kept as a pet, it gave some aid in hunting, and it provided an occasional dish of fresh meat. It also furnished the skins used in the winter cloaks worn by persons of high rank. Like the Australian dingo, it appears to be a domesticated strain of the feral dog of India. It is now extinct in New Zealand, but a dog similar to it may be seen in New Guinea villages, particularly those on the mountain plateaux.

LANAI, men from. While there is no direct evidence that adventurous men from the Hawaiian Islands did voyage as far south as New Zealand, there must have been voyages from Hawai'i to Tahiti and back at the time with which this story deals. The channel between the big island of Maui and the smaller Kahoolawe was named by the Hawaiians "Road to Tahiti." The authors do not regard it as improbable that a canoe captain from Lanai, on being informed by the Tahitians that a great land lay to the south-west, would set sail in that direction to see it for himself. Hence the inclusion of such an episode in this story.

MANA. This term cannot be defined by any single word in English, since it covers prestige, power, ability, morale, and what is known as 'face' in the East. If a man lost his mana, as did a great fighting chief when his forces were defeated in battle, it was regarded as a dreadful calamity. In our civilized society a counterpart of mana can be recognized in the way in which some people become fashion-leaders. We can see it also in the hero-worship of the champion athlete, the person with wealth, the screen star, the gangster 'big-shot,' and the owner of successful racehorses. Loss of mana among us can be seen likewise, as such people are forgotten or cold-shouldered when they no longer have the world at their feet.

MANAHUNE, or MENAHUNE (pages 139–140). Polynesian legends relate how their explorers and pioneer settlers found a backward people in possession of some Pacific islands. Their presence was probably due to what is known as 'Drift voyages.' These were caused when canoes, setting off on what was intended to be a brief trip between two adjacent islands, were driven into the open sea by a sudden storm. In some cases, by a combination of luck and endurance, a canoe would eventually reach a distant, uninhabited island. Not having domestic livestock, seeds, or food plants with them, such people would have a struggle to exist if the island had no native plants to serve as substitutes for cultivated fruits and vegetables. Later arrivals, bringing pigs, fowls, vegetable seeds, and cuttings of fruit-trees, looked down on the original settlers, who had been forced to revert to a primitive existence. The Tangata Whenua (Maruiwi) whom the ancestors of the Maori found in New Zealand appear to have been somewhat degenerate descendants of Polynesians whose canoes had been driven there by a great storm. As recently as 1930 Rennell and Bellona islands were still populated by a backward people of Polynesian stock.

Some very ancient legends, however, describe the Manahune as a small, shy people who lived in the forests. This would probably refer to the little Negrito jungle folk whom the Polynesians encountered during their migrations from South-east Asia to the Pacific. The term 'Manahune' would seem, therefore, to have been applied to two distinct types of people.

MAORI WARS caused by old women. The case of the elderly shrews of the Manianga in this book can be taken as typical. Among many native races much of the fighting was fomented by the older women, who were usually spiteful and very resentful of real or imagined slights. Quite frequently the American Indian braves would have settled intertribal disputes by negotiation, but they fought it out because the old squaws would jeer at them if they returned without the scalps of slain enemies. Viragoes among the Australian aborigines acted in the same way, while the old women of some Maori tribes were notorious. Here is a typical case: An old woman named Koraria was sitting outside the Puke-Tapu pa. A party of men belonging to the Awa, a neighbouring clan, walked past. One made a joking remark. Koraria took it seriously and replied with insults. When the Awa men returned to their pa and repeated what Koraria had said, their own old women were furious. They insisted that a war party attack Puke-Tapu as a reprisal. It was done, and several men on both sides were killed. In retaliation, and again egged on by old women, Puke-Tapu then attacked the Warahoe clan, who were related to the Awa, but who had no more to do with the quarrel than the man in the moon. In this way a whole district was set fighting. When it ended at last, hundreds of young men had been killed. A similar psychological kink on the part of elderly females is not unknown as an underlying cause of disputes among civilized family groups.

MAT-WEAVING (page 19). In the technical sense true weaving was unknown among the Polynesians. Its place was taken by a form of plaiting. Mat-making was regarded as the highest of the domestic arts. In Samoa, where the people cling more to their traditions and the ways of their ancestors than anywhere else in the Pacific, it still holds pride of place. Elsewhere—unfortunately—it is dying out or has become almost a lost art.

Many of these mats measure six or seven feet in length by three or four in breadth. In texture they resemble a coarse linen. Some are used to sleep on, and a pile of them forms the seat of a high chief. The very best are stored away, as we would keep examples of fine embroidery, to be brought out only on special occasions or to show to visitors.

MIGRATIONS, causes of. The three main reasons for human migrations have been woven into this story. In order of significance, they are:

(1) Population pressure. The climates of large portions of the earth's surface are slowly but inexorably changing. In the days before large-scale importations of food were possible, peoples would multiply their numbers during long runs of favourable seasons, but find themselves overcrowded and even faced with starvation when lean years arrived or the rainfall diminished. On small islands the same thing could occur very rapidly through overtaxing of the local food resources. Population pressure was then felt. More recently the same thing has manifested itself more in lack of opportunities in a crowded homeland. In the last hundred and fifty years it has helped to fill America and Australia with people of Western European descent. In the past thirty years it has driven some Japanese to migrate to Brazil and form colonies in the wilder regions of that country.

(2) Defeat in battle. In the past the survivors on the losing side in a war have often been forced to flee in order to save their lives. So have persecuted minorities. This is still happening, as witness refugees from behind the Iron Curtain.

(3) Ambition. Many younger sons, seeing no hope of advancement at home, set out to seek wider opportunities in a new land. In the case of Polynesians and other races in a similar high state of culture, when younger sons of chiefs set off to find a land of their own they were accompanied by some faithful followers, the nucleus of a new tribe.

These three forces can be deduced from archæological evidence unearthed on prehistoric sites, traced in legends, and stand revealed throughout the course of recorded history.

MNEMONICS, or Memory Aids. These were used to a certain extent among primitive races, and were quite common among people who, while in a high state of culture, had not evolved or acquired a system of writing. In South America, the Marquesas, and Hawai'i the knotted cord (quipu) was used. As an aid to remembering his long list of illustrious ancestors the high-born Maori used a carved staff with a row of notches along the edge. We still use forms of this ancient device. One example is our "Thirty days hath September" rhyme. Another is the knot in a handkerchief to remind us to post a letter or bring home that reel of sewing-cotton.

PERERE'S TRIP. The Polynesians undoubtedly visited the south-eastern part of Australia. Stone adze-blades, of the distinctive type made by these people, have been found among sand-dunes on the coast of New South Wales; at Green Point, near Port MacDonnell, at the bottom end of South Australia; on the coast near Adelaide; and on the bank of the Murray at Gunbower, Victoria. Further evidence is the "Kangaroo rat" game among the aborigines of Southern Australia, played by throwing along the ground a long, thin stick with an end shaped like an aerial bomb. This is identical with the Tika game of Polynesia. A Polynesian influence in basket-weaving can also be seen among some southern aboriginal tribes in Australia. The islands which Perere is described as visiting are Lord Howe and Norfolk. Polynesian-type stone implements have been found on the latter.

POLYNESIAN CULTURE. The Polynesian people, as they were when first seen by Europeans, form a striking instance of a culture in a state of arrested development. Their high intelligence, coupled with their well-exhibited powers of abstract thought—a thing usually little evident in the more primitive races—their cast of features, their build, and their light skins, all point to a relationship with some of the people of South-east Asia, as well as their having been originally an offshoot of one of those parent civilizations in the Euphrates–Caucasus–Indus Valley areas where agriculture first arose. When the early seaborne migrations of the Polynesians took place, perhaps as far back as 5000 years ago, they were probably in a state of culture similar to that of the pre-Homeric Greeks. They would know only a rudimentary form of agriculture, using the hoe and digging-stick method of cultivating the soil which was employed before the invention of the plough. But where the Greeks, having gained the hybrid virility brought about by intermarriage with other good human strains, fell heirs to the ancient civilizations of Crete, Egypt, Sumeria, and Babylonia, then built upon this excellent foundation such a vast edifice of new knowledge that they passed on to the world the greatest cultural heritage of all time, the Polynesians sailed away into unknown seas. For lack of the necessary ores they lost the art of metal-working and reverted to tools of polished stone, but some of the latter were still made in shapes bearing an unmistakable resemblance to Bronze Age types. In the Pacific they were cut off from the stimulus of contact with other cultures. A further handicap was living on islands far apart. Their culture does not seem to have degenerated, except in a few isolated instances, but they made little progress after reaching a cultural backwater in the Pacific. A parallel case can be seen in the inhabitants of the Outer Hebrides in Great Britain. There the people still maintain many primitive ways of life which were superseded more than a thousand years ago in the chief centres of British culture.

POLYNESIAN RELIGIOUS BELIEFS. The original religion of these people consisted of a pantheon of gods and goddesses, very similar to those worshipped by the Greeks. At their head was a supreme being, known as Io or a variant of the name. It provides a most interesting study, for in it we can see how human beings, when they reach a high state of culture, realize that some great and universal being, presence, or power must lie behind the whole of creation. Unfortunately, the early-day missionaries dealt a shattering blow to the morale of the Polynesian race by decrying all these old beliefs when they introduced Christianity. They also frowned on the harmless pleasures of the people. All forms of dancing were banned; even the wearing of flowers in the hair was prohibited. Nowadays the good missionaries, guided by anthropologists, graft the fundamentals of Christianity on to the best of the old beliefs of a native race, with results which are almost invariably happy and successful. Further, legislation now prohibits missionaries from reverting to the killjoy policy which was so disastrous in the past.

POLYNESIANS, origin of. It is extremely probable that these people came originally from South-east Asia. To-day they are found scattered over a vast area of the Pacific, from Easter Island to Hawai'i, and from New Zealand to Botel Tobago, off the coast of Formosa. All speak dialects of the same mother tongue, which is related to the Austric group of languages, still surviving among scattered peoples of Southern Asia. In postulating an American origin for the Polynesians Thor Heyerdahl, of *Kon Tiki* fame, failed to account for several vital things. Groups of people of an unmistakable Polynesian type are found to-day on Madagascar, off the east coast of Africa, as well as on islands such as Engano, off the west coast of Sumatra. This points to an origin at some place midway between the two, with South-east Asia as the obvious spot. The islands of Indonesia, which they used as a temporary settlement on the way to the Pacific, are the homeland of the wild ancestors of more than one of the food plants cultivated by the Polynesians. Further, South-east Asia is the only place where they could have obtained the types of dogs, pigs, and fowls which were their domestic livestock. The most likely cause for the original migrations was an invasion by great hordes of some aggressive, land-hungry folk armed with bows and arrows. Against them the Polynesians, probably living in scattered coastal village communities, could make no effective resistance. They were forced to sail off in search of a new homeland. Why the Polynesians did not adopt the bow as a weapon of war is a mystery. On some islands they knew of it, but used it only as a toy.

POLYNESIANS, racial characteristics. The people of Polynesia and Micronesia are a so-called 'dark-white' folk, whose exposed skin tans to a golden brown, very close to the tint acquired by young men and women on Australian surf beaches. They are related to the Mediterranean race, a type of man who once lived over much of the area from India to Spain. The Southern Italians who have migrated to Australia in such numbers of late years are modified descendants of the same stock. Some Polynesians show traces of admixture with Papuan peoples. When the latter strain is strong we have the so-called dark Melanesians, who predominate in the Solomon Islands, the New Hebrides, and Fiji. In Micronesia the people show traces of Mongolian characteristics, probably due to admixture with drift voyagers and stranded crews from the direction of Formosa and China. How this could happen was illustrated a few years ago. A sailing-junk was blown out to sea while voyaging along the coast of China. The crew were found still alive in their craft off the coast of California. Polynesians are noted for their physical beauty. The leading families claim great purity of stock, and some chiefs can quote genealogies running back eighty, ninety, and even more than a hundred generations. Prior to the most remote ancestor mentioned in the family tree they identify themselves with the original deities of their religious pantheon. In character they are laughter-loving, and those living in the tropics regard life as something to be enjoyed as much as possible. They work to acquire the everyday, fundamental needs in the way of food, clothing, and shelter, but they fail to see any sense in toiling merely to amass a pile of worldly goods. Of all human beings they are probably the least jealous by nature, nor do they strive to outdo one another except in the friendly rivalry of sport. 'Keeping up with the people next door' finds no place in their outlook. The Maori branch of the race, stimulated by a cooler climate and driven by necessity, are more competitive and acquisitive. In full competition with the people of European descent some Polynesians have had distinguished careers as statesmen, lawyers, and doctors. Nearly all Polynesians have a natural dignity and courtesy, coupled—especially in the Maori—with a strong and quite justified pride of race.

POUNAMU (greenstone). From very early times nephrite and jade have been highly valued. At first it was due to the fact that these very hard and exceedingly tough rocks made better blades for tools than any other stones. In addition to taking a keen edge they were not liable to break or chip when used. Later, as metals came into use, jades were still valued for their translucent beauty and colour. Pieces were worked into ornaments. In New Zealand, only the form of jade known as nephrite occurs. The Maori called it Pounamu and valued it for its appearance as well as for its use as tool blades. Known locally to-day as greenstone, it is found as boulders in the beds

of a few rivers on the west coast of the South Island. The
Maori living in the North Island had to obtain it by barter or
by sending out special expeditions to secure it. Large blocks
were broken by using heavy stone mauls. The pieces were then
sawn into shape, either by using grit embedded in the edges of
wooden laths or by rubbing with thin slabs of sandstone. Because of its hardness weeks of labour were required to fashion
a tool blade. Greenstone weapons and implements were cherished for generations, being thought to be endowed with the
mana of all those who had used them in the past.

RATS AS FOOD. The kiore rat, taken to New Zealand by the
ancestors of the Maori, must not be confused with our repul-
sive pest rat. It was a small, vegetarian animal, no more objec-
tionable as food than a rabbit. It is now extinct in New
Zealand, except on a small island off the coast, having been
exterminated by the introduced pest rats.

RAW FISH as substitute for water (page 64). This expedient
for quenching thirst was often used on long canoe voyages. It
has also been used by our seamen when forced to take to the
lifeboats by the sinking of a ship. The raw meat contains a
high proportion of liquid free from salt. It sustains life if this
plasma is extracted from the fibres by chewing. The drinking
of sea water, except in small quantities at long intervals,
usually hastens exhaustion and death.

RICE. The original staple food of the Polynesians, as described by Rehua, could have been rice, for it grows in wet
ground and vari (or fari) is a very ancient Indian name for this
grain. Once the Polynesians had discovered the breadfruit, a
native of Indonesia, the laborious planting and cultivation of
rice crops would be unnecessary.

STARS, dates fixed by. The Polynesian calendar, like that
of the ancient Egyptians, was based upon the first appearance each year of some well-known star or constellation in
the eastern sky at dawn. Known as the 'heliacal rising' of a
star, this method is accurate to the day. The New Year was
marked by the heliacal rising of the Pleiades (Seven Sisters)
group of stars. Among all the pioneer agriculturists of the
Middle East the first appearance of the Pleiades at dawn each
year was the sign that the time to prepare for sowing the crops

had arrived, so it may be a very ancient idea indeed. Among Australian aborigines the heliacal rising of the Pleiades is associated with the annual appearance of dingo puppies, which they regard as a very choice article of diet. Whenever we can trace any such fundamental belief of mankind to its source, we usually find a direct association with the all-important quest for food.

TAPA. This most useful material was usually made from the fibrous inner (cambium) layer of the bark of the paper mulberry, but coarser cloths were made from the bark of the breadfruit and the hibiscus. The method of manufacture has been described in the text. During Captain Cook's explorations in the Pacific the chiefs of the islands which he visited made him many presents of tapa cloth. When he brought them to England samples of them were bound into books and distributed to learned societies and museums. To-day those volumes are ethnological treasures. Adelaide is fortunate in possessing two copies, one in the South Australian Museum and the other owned by the South Australian Branch of the Royal Geographical Society of Australasia. An examination of their contents shows the coarser specimens to be like rough blotting-paper, but the best ones, worn by chiefs and their wives, were almost as fine as muslin.

TAPU, or TABU. A complex subject. Among very primitive peoples it marked the emergence of both religious beliefs and a legal system to replace the 'jungle-law' rule of the strongest individuals. It is the "unclean" of the Old Testament. Basically tapu is a legal code which needs no police force to see that its provisions are obeyed. Law-courts are not necessary to award punishments for breaches, for it is believed that anyone who breaks a tapu brings upon himself the wrath of the gods. As peoples reached higher stages of culture, tapu extended its ramifications, and some of its ukases became quite senseless, such as the prohibition against a woman touching a fishing-canoe or the deplorable Maori neglect of the sick. The persons and possessions of chiefs were protected by tapu, as were the spots where notable people had been buried. In order to conserve supplies some foods were tapu at certain seasons. Most of the ridiculous prohibitions seem to have been initiated by priests in an arbitrary demonstration of their power. Our modern applications of the sensible side of tapu can be seen in: (1) "Keep off the Grass" and "No Smoking" notices; (2) the words "Ladies" and "Gentlemen" on the doors of retiring-rooms; (3) traffic-control lights at busy intersections; (4) fishery and game regulations, with the total protection of some species of birds and animals.

TOPS AS POLYNESIAN TOYS. When Captain Cook visited New Zealand he was astonished to find Maori boys playing with a whip-top of a type which he had used in his own child-hood. Since then we have learned that this type of top had a widespread distribution, being popular in Indonesia as well as in other parts of the world. The Maori may have invented this toy independently, but it is more likely that the idea was acquired from some other people during the Polynesian migra-tions. (*See also* Culture, diffusion of.)

UTU. Among the Maori, utu vengeance corresponded to the vendetta of Sicily, the American feud, or the "Eye for an eye, tooth for a tooth" of the Old Testament. Unfortunately for the peace of the country, the Maori was not content to repay an injury with another of the same kind. If somebody knocked out one of his teeth he wanted the other fellow to lose *all* his teeth as a reprisal, then to be condemned to live on the toughest of food for the rest of his days. A dreadful example is provided by the case of Hongi Hika, chief of the Ngapuhi tribe. When he was a boy his mother had impressed on him that he had a sacred duty to avenge the death of Tahapango, his grand-father, who had been slain by the northern tribes. Hongi visited London and was given many valuable presents. On the way home he sold these gifts in Sydney and purchased muskets with which to arm his followers. Then he exacted utu by attacking the tribes which had killed Tahapango. After this he turned his firearms against the southern tribes to avenge the death of other relatives. Between ten and twenty thousand of his fellow human beings were slain by Hongi as a reprisal for the deaths of a few relations.

BOOKS FOR FURTHER READING

For those who would like to learn more about the history, arts, customs, religious beliefs, and daily life of the people who explored and colonized the Pacific during the period 1000 B.C.–A.D. 1350 the following works are recommended:

GENERAL

Typee, by Herman Melville. Undoubtedly the best book concerning the Polynesians as they were before having any close contact with Europeans. Over a century ago Melville lived for months among a tribe in the Marquesas Islands. This book is a record of his stay. Many other Europeans lived in the same way among natives, but usually they were either low, ignorant types or lacked the ability to observe and record. Melville was a happy exception. Well educated, well read, and a keen observer, he was also a gifted writer. As a result he passed on to posterity this literary and anthropological treasure. (Various publishers.)

Polynesian Paradise, by Donald Sloane. A modern account of living among Polynesians who still follow the ways of their ancestors. Unfortunately, this book is now rare and is sought by collectors, so it is hard to secure a copy. (Robert Hale, 1941.)

Queen Salote and Her Kingdom, by Sir Harry Luke. The work of a former High Commissioner for the Western Pacific, this gives a very bright account of the history of the independent kingdom of Tonga and its gracious, talented Queen. (Putnam, London, 1954.)

Vikings of the Sunrise, by Sir Peter Buck. Written by a distinguished scientist whose part-Maori ancestry gave him a deep insight into Polynesian psychology, this is an outstanding work, but several statements in it must be modified in the light of later discoveries. One is that the extinct Tasmanians could not have reached their island home by land travel. To-day we know that they did reach it by travelling across Australia. Nor is it certain that the Polynesians must have reached the Central Pacific by way of the atolls of Micronesia, as Buck claimed. To-day we have evidence that some came by the shorter and obvious route along the northern coast of New Guinea, but could not settle on the mainland for the reason given in our book: A single canoe, carrying no more than twenty fighting-men, cannot occupy land already in the possession of numerous hostile savages. But the crews could, and did, settle for a time on small outlying islands previously uninhabited. This explains how the food plants from Indonesia, which could not survive long voyages from atoll to atoll, were transported to the Central Pacific. (Whitcombe and Tombs, New Zealand, 1954.)

The Coming of the Maori, by Sir Peter Buck. Shortly before his death a few years ago Buck completed this book. It incorporates the latest discoveries and deductions concerning the Polynesian migrations to New Zealand, with most able descriptions of old-time Maori culture. One of the best books ever written about a native people. (Whitcombe and Tombs, New Zealand, 1952.)

POLYNESIAN ASTRONOMY AND NAVIGATION

The Morning Star Rises, by Maud Makemsom. (Oxford University Press, Yale University Press, 1942.)

The Raft Book, by Harold Gatty. (George Grady Press, New York, 1943.)

THE MAORI PEOPLE

The Maori As He Was, by Elsdon Best. An admirable book, in which some misconceptions in the original two-volume work have been corrected in accordance with recent discoveries. (New Zealand Board of Science and Art, 1924.)

Old New Zealand, by F. Maning. An account of life among the Maori during the early days of European settlement in New Zealand. A faithful picture of these people at the time. (Whitcombe and Tombs, New Zealand, 1951.)

The Moa-hunter Period of Maori Culture, by Dr Roger Duff. The most modern work on the early Maori, in which ancient tradition is supported and amplified by critical scientific excavations of old village and burial sites. Apart from its wealth of information it is a fine example of how the scientist can bring the dead past to life. (Department of Internal Affairs, New Zealand, 1950.)

POLYNESIAN ANTHROPOLOGY

Coming of Age in Samoa, by Dr Margaret Mead. Some parts of this work are far too mature for young readers to grasp the full implications of Dr Mead's studies, but other portions describe, in pleasant detail, the course of child life in a Polynesian community, with its joys, problems of adolescence, successes and failures. (Penguin Books, London, 1944.)

CAPTAIN COOK'S VOYAGES

After reading the works mentioned you are recommended to read the *Voyages* of Captain Cook in their original, unabridged form. His writings contain an immense amount of information about the Polynesians as they were before they lost much of their original culture, but in order to derive the greatest benefit it is necessary to know something of the subject. As was only natural in one who was seeing a strange race for the first time and who had no previous research whatsoever to guide him, Cook set down many misconceptions, and his spellings of the names of persons and places are confusing to the uninitiated. He frequently wrote down the full reply as being the name. Hence his "Otaheite" for "Tahiti," the "O" being the Polynesian equivalent for our "It is. . . ." But anyone who has read authoritative modern works or who has had personal contact with some branch of the Polynesian people can see through Cook's errors and gain additional benefit from the writings of one of the world's most notable explorers. His *Voyages* should not be confused with his *Journals*, however. The former are written in the style of the old-type travel book, but the latter merely record his voyages in the terse language of the ship's logbook.